CW00544177

EXHAUSTED

EXHAUSTED

An A–Z for the Weary

ANNA KATHARINA SCHAFFNER

Profile Books

First published in Great Britain in 2024 by
Profile Books Ltd
29 Cloth Fair
London
ECIA 7JQ

www.profilebooks.com

1 3 5 7 9 10 8 6 4 2

Typeset in Sabon by MacGuru Ltd
Printed and bound in Great Britain by Clays Ltd, Elcograf S.p.A.

A CIP catalogue record for this book is available
from the British Library.

ISBN 978 1 80081 690 9
eISBN 978 1 80081 692 3

FSC
www.fsc.org
MIX
Paper | Supporting
responsible forestry
FSC® C018072

For my wonderful coaching clients

Contents

Introduction

Do you feel tired and exhausted all or much of the time? Are you living to work, rather than working to live? Have your to-do lists and responsibilities become an unmanageable burden, filling you with dread? Are you feeling disengaged and demotivated? Perhaps you find yourself constantly questioning your accomplishments and skills, adding inner noise to outer stressors? If so, then this book is for you. It brings together insights, both old and new, into the causes of and cures for our collective exhaustion, and will, I hope, inspire you to find new ways to overcome that state and to revitalise yourself. For exhaustion threatens the very core of our being: if we feel lacking in energy, strength and time, we switch into a zombie-like survival mode. We become alienated from our emotions and desires and lose sight of what really matters to us and what makes us happy.

First of all, know that you are not alone. For the bleary-eyed are legion. Exhaustion in general, and its modern-day offspring burnout more specifically, are among the most prevalent ills of our age. Because work tends to dominate most of our lives and thoughts, and also because almost everything can feel like work these days, burnout has become the most talked-about exhaustion-syndrome of our times. A recent report by the American Psychological

Association found that burnout and stress are at an all-time high across professions, having been significantly heightened by the Covid-19 pandemic.[1] I, too, used to be exhausted all the time. My mind had turned to ash, my life seemed flat and dull and work felt interminable. Although I had a permanent job at the university in theory, the threat of redundancy had been hanging over my head for half a decade. While our student numbers steadily shrank each year, my anxiety and stress levels increased. I spent a lot of time worrying about what I could do instead, and I could think of very little. In addition, the fear of losing our jobs created a toxic culture at work, which, combined with feelings of helplessness, loss of purpose and fear of unemployment, is of course a perfect recipe for burnout. I came to know that state intimately.

Strictly speaking, burnout is an occupational malaise – a state of exhaustion caused by chronic stress at work. Research has shown that, in the vast majority of cases, the causes of burnout are not our faulty coping mechanisms – as the happiness industry wishes to make us believe – but are deeply rooted in our working environments.[2] The top five reasons for burnout are unfair treatment at work, unmanageable workloads, lack of role clarity, poor communication and support, and unreasonable time pressures.[3] We can also burn out because we feel we lack control and agency, or because we experience a clash of values.[4] Burnout is often related to violations of our dignity at work, and to a feeling that we are not valued. Most of us do not suffer burnout on account of our bad stress management skills, but because the structures in which we are embedded are making us ill.

Yet what happens to us at work is rarely the only cause of our exhaustion. The deeper origins of chronic or recurring exhaustion tend to be more complex, involving both outer and inner factors that may not be limited to the world of work. Sometimes, we can be our own bad bosses, having internalised injurious attitudes to work. Our current burnout culture is rooted in deeper and older beliefs about time and productivity, which affect us even if we are not working for others.

We may also be depleted because we use up too much of our energy in internal psychological warfare – battles between different parts of ourselves with conflicting aims and values. That was definitely true in my case. I was exhausted by an unkind voice in my head, constantly questioning everything I achieved, dragging my accomplishments into the mud. That hounding inner voice is in fact very common. It has many names – internal critic, cruel superego, inner demon, saboteur, judge and negative self-talk. Whatever we prefer to call it, the good news is that there are strategies for reducing our inner critic's draining impact, and finding ways to project our energy outwards, towards the people and projects we care about. Ultimately, that is what overcoming exhaustion is all about: replenishing and freeing up our energy so that we can consciously choose how to use it.

I have always been interested in psychology, especially in our shadows – the less conscious parts of our psyches, our individual and collective blind spots. Partly to make sense of my own chronic exhaustion, and as part of my continued work as a cultural historian, I wrote a book on exhaustion's long history.[5] I was interested in tracing our current beliefs about energy, time, work and productivity back to their origins. More recently, I published a book on the ancient art of self-improvement – much of which revolves around strategies for directing our energies outwards, rather than being passive victims of our unconscious patterns and fears.[6] While I love the deep history of psychology, I also grew ever more interested in its living practice. I dabbled in psychoanalysis for a while and then trained as a coach. Eventually, I started my own coaching practice and specialised in helping the exhausted. Much in the tradition of the wounded healer, we tend to want to teach what we ourselves have to learn. In this A–Z, I share with you my own favourite reflections on exhaustion – ranging from ancient wisdom, theological treatises and philosophical and literary works to insights from my own coaching practice and the latest scientific research on stress and burnout.

We may be forgiven for thinking of our own time as the age of exhaustion par excellence – defined, as it is, by an all-pervasive cultural overvaluation of work, highly addictive information and communication technologies and the endless psycho-social pressures of neo-liberal capitalism. Recently we have seen an unprecedented rise in depression, chronic stress and burnout in the workplace. Lockdown-related home-working has not helped. Work seems to have infiltrated all aspects of our lives. What is more, increasingly, we see our whole lives through the lens of work: we tend to think of ever more processes as effortful labour – including our relationships with partners, friends and our children, our health and fitness and our psychological and spiritual development. We often feel we must excel in and 'work on' all of these areas, and this choice of words is telling. The psychoanalyst Josh Cohen writes: 'Working, understood as both labour and functionality, is now the imperative of our time.'[7]

Cohen describes burnout as a 'small apocalypse of the soul' – an inner inferno that can also constitute a moment of rebellion against the injunction to work at all times.[8] By contrast, rather than viewing it as a temporary crisis, the journalist Anne Helen Petersen argues that burnout is the foundational condition for millennials today. In a 2019 BuzzFeed article that went viral, she illuminates the structural economic causes of the current burnout epidemic amongst her generation.[9] Burnout occurs, Petersen writes, 'when the distance between the ideal and the possible lived reality becomes too much to bear'.[10] The social contract is broken: education is no longer a safe pathway to social mobility and stable middle-class employment. Millennials are the first generation in modern times that is financially worse off than their parents. All the stories on which they were brought up – that hard work always pays, that the best succeed in a meritocratic free market, that all will be well if only they find jobs they love – have imploded.

It is true that we seem to live in particularly dark and fast-moving times. There are several serious crises that threaten the way of life we are used to – climate change, war, pandemics, economic uncertainty and growing political polarisation are chief amongst them. Yet exhaustion is in fact a ubiquitous and timeless phenomenon. It features at the centre of a range of past and current syndromes, including not just burnout but also melancholia, acedia, neurasthenia and depression. Writers and thinkers across the ages have claimed to be exhausted and look back nostalgically to periods in the past that they imagine as less wearying. Reflections on the limited nature of our energies, and the internal and external causes that may deplete them, can be traced all the way back to ancient China.

The critic Frank Kermode writes:

> We think of our own crisis as pre-eminent, more worrying, more interesting than other crises. ... It is commonplace to talk about our historical situation as uniquely terrible and in a way privileged, a cardinal point in time. But can it really be so? It seems doubtful that our crisis ... is one of the important differences between us and our predecessors. Many of them felt as we do. If the evidence looks good to us, so it did to them.[11]

Although our ancestors may have used different images and metaphors to describe the experience, I found it immensely comforting to learn that we are not the only ones to have struggled with exhaustion. People in many historical periods and across cultures have wrestled with exhaustion, speculated about its origins and devised cures and therapies for overcoming it. The good news is that we still have much to learn from the ancients, and from other cultures.

What changes through history is not the experience of exhaustion as such, but rather the metaphors we use to describe it and the stories we tell to explain its causes. Theories of exhaustion, moreover, are also powerful barometers for dominant cultural anxieties and aspirations. They often concentrate on very specific cultural discontents. In our age, for example, the focus tends to be on addictive tech, the psychological effects of relentless growth imperatives and worries about our ever more porous work–life balance. But in the past, people were concerned about the adverse effects of brain work, evil noon-day demons, lukewarm religious faith, too spicy diets, overexciting novels, gory news stories, motor cars, female emancipation and the insidious impact of the planet Saturn.

Lastly, different theories of exhaustion can also yield insights into how we think about our agency and willpower. Do we pin our exhaustion predominantly to inner or outer causes? Do we think of exhaustion as mainly a mind, body or a broader cultural phenomenon? Do we believe that we can influence the things that deplete us, or do we see ourselves as victims of vampiric forces that are beyond our control? The stories we tell about our exhaustion matter, for they shape our experience of it and the actions we take to counter it.

In this A–Z you will therefore not only find reflections on the latest psychological research on stress and burnout, but also encounter the thoughts of listless monks, weary melancholics, Renaissance alchemists and overstimulated neurasthenics. You will meet fictional figures such as Bartleby, Dante and Oblomov – all of whom are guides with precious wisdom to share. I strongly believe that to overcome our own exhaustion, we need mixed mental arts

– both old and new perspectives, drawn from science, literature, philosophy and psychology. For new is not always better. Often, it is the timeless ancient models that hold the key to our present-day challenges. After all, our species has struggled with exhaustion since the beginning of time.

The writer Jonathan Malesic argues that burnout is a cultural rather than individual problem.[12] It is in fact both. The roots of our exhaustion are often anchored in deeper cultural beliefs, which, in turn, shape our individual behaviours. This A–Z is a self-help book, but one that seeks to explore our shared cultural assumptions around work, exhaustion and productivity. We have underestimated the healing power of philosophical reflections and historical and sociological insights for far too long. They have to become active curative ingredients in our attempts to tackle our exhaustion, and can help us to see our problems from a different perspective. Shifts in perspective, both subtle and large, can propel us out of our paralysis and enable us to take action. Not everything is our personal responsibility, and nor are many of the dilemmas with which we wrestle unique to us. Many of the factors that cause our exhaustion are structural and cultural in nature. What is more, some of the beliefs that are making us ill are not just the product of recent neo-liberal efficiency enhancement drives. They are much older than we think, their roots reaching far back in time.

The essayist, poet and activist Audre Lorde writes: 'There is no such thing as a single-issue struggle because we do not lead single-issue lives.'[13] This is also true of our exhaustion – it has multiple and complex causes, both inner and outer in nature. I exclude from my discussion cases of exhaustion that are the result of clearly identifiable medical conditions. Exhaustion that is not obviously traceable to one singular cause, however, requires a transdisciplinary and systemic approach that doesn't just focus on outer or inner factors but explores the ways in which they intersect. A fast-growing number of researchers are now analysing the ways in which social and cultural forces shape our mental well-being.[14] I believe that they also have to feature much more prominently in our self-help literature.

As a culture, we fetishise productivity and efficiency to such an extent that this overvaluation has dramatically backfired and is making an increasing number of us ill. 'Our bodies and minds are overworked by more than work', Josh Cohen writes. 'They are subject to a culture that relates to every moment as an opportunity to produce or consume.'[15] Most of us are so burnt out because we are entangled in what are essentially very damaging assumptions about time and how to use it. These beliefs have become so normalised that we think of them simply as natural, as the way things are. The American writer David Foster Wallace beautifully captures what such naturalised ideology may feel like:

> There are these two young fish swimming along and they happen to meet an older fish swimming the other way, who nods at them and says, 'Morning boys. How's the water?' And the two young fish swim on for a bit, and then eventually one of them looks over at the other and goes, 'What the hell is water?'[16]

My hope for this book is that it will help you to see more clearly the water in which we all swim and that makes us so very tired.

This guide comprises a series of exhaustion-themed mini-essays that cover topics such as capitalism, energy, joy, life-cost, rest, time, perfectionism and work. It invites you to learn both from cutting-edge research and from history and ancient wisdom. You can dip in and out of this *A–Z* at your leisure and start with whichever topic calls you first. The order in which you read the entries does not matter. Because I know that your energies are likely to be limited, all entries are short. I recommend that you read no more than one a day. That way, the ideas you will encounter can properly sink in and slowly seed new perspectives. Over the course of a month or so, they will gradually change your perception of your own exhaustion. Most importantly, they will alter how you feel about it. For all true transformation must result in changes to the structure of our feelings. Knowledge that lives just in the head is useless. The German writer Goethe observed that 'Knowing is not enough; we must apply. Willing is not enough; we must do.' For that reason, you will also encounter practical advice to help you take concrete steps towards restoring your state of vitality.

This book would not have been possible without my wonderful coaching clients – all the exhausted writers, academics, activists, painters, doctors, founders, soldiers, lawyers, managers and CEOs with whom I have had the privilege to work over the years. I have learned so much from all of you. Theory is one thing, but lived experience and how to deal with it in all its maddening messiness and surprising beauty is quite another. You know who you are – thank you for sharing your struggles, wisdom and insights.

A is for Acceptance

When we find ourselves slowed and weakened by exhaustion, the first step is to accept that we can't keep on doing what has brought us to this point. Exhaustion is a warning sign, both from the body and the mind. It is an injunction to pause and to seek rest. If we are truly burnt out, we may find ourselves unable to concentrate or even to engage in any work-related tasks at all. Our body is saying no, refusing to function until we have addressed the underlying issues. By breaking down, it seeks to protect us from further injury and wishes to communicate something. But what exactly is our exhaustion trying to tell us?

It may well be truths that are hard to hear. When we have given our all, and more, to professions for which we have trained and which have been the focus of all our striving and passion, it can be deeply threatening to imagine a future that entails doing something else. It may also be near-impossible for us to envisage how we could live and work differently, or how we might begin the arduous task of establishing more solid personal boundaries, which can entail conflict for which we have neither the appetite nor the energy. We may not even be prepared to admit that we aren't really coping with the many demands on our time and attention, and strive instead to keep going, no matter at what cost. We might also have to take a sober, unflinching look at our coping strategies, which may well be exacerbating our problems. 'What if the way we respond to the crisis is part of the crisis?' the philosopher Bayo Akomolafe asks.[1] Perhaps we are leaning too hard on alcohol, work, shopping or comfort eating to manage the chronic stressors in our lives. We may have turned into procrastinators or avoiders, or else succumbed to feelings of bitterness and resentment.

Whatever our exhaustion is trying to tell us, the starting point on our journey back to vitality must be to accept that there is a problem. Next, we need to decide which parts of our circumstances are and which are not under our control, and then focus our remaining energy on what we can control. The Stoic philosopher Epictetus sums this up neatly: 'Within our power are opinion, motivation, desire, aversion, and, in a word, whatever is of our own doing; not within our power are our body, our property, reputation, office, and, in a word, whatever is not of our own doing.'[2] In other words, what tends to be within our control is our inner life, our judgements, our reactions and how we treat others, while most other things, including what people think of us, are not. This insight alone is a hard pill to swallow, for most of us like to assume that we have much more agency and control over our lives than we do.

If the causes of our exhaustion are mainly internal, such as an overactive inner critic or a tendency to catastrophise, we can benefit from seeing a therapist or a coach, or seek to train our hearts and minds on our own. The Buddhist psychologist Tara Brach understands radical acceptance as learning to recognise what is true in the present moment and cultivating mindfulness and compassion. Radical acceptance is about being fully aware of what is happening within our bodies and minds at any given moment, without judging or seeking to control it. It entails feeling sorrow and pain without resisting it, and regarding what is happening with an open and loving heart. Brach writes:

> Radical Acceptance reverses our habit of living at war with experiences that are unfamiliar, frightening or intense. It is the necessary antidote to years of neglecting ourselves, years of judging and treating ourselves harshly, years of rejecting this moment's experience. Radical Acceptance is the willingness to experience ourselves and our life as it is.[3]

But if the causes of our exhaustion are external, the matter becomes more complex. While many of us will be affected by both inner and outer stressors, it is highly likely that a large part of our exhaustion is rooted in work-related matters. These include unmanageable task loads, unreasonable deadlines and a lack of autonomy and appreciation. We may suffer continuous moral injury in jobs we cannot leave for financial reasons. We may also be sick of people telling us to strengthen our resilience, to breathe deeply and to establish firmer boundaries between our work and our home life. But what, then, are we to do when we cannot realistically change the external causes of our exhaustion?

Audre Lorde writes: 'Nothing I accept about myself can be used against me to diminish me.' Practising radical acceptance of what we can't change is not defeatism. Instead, it is a wise decision that allows us to direct our energy towards what is within our control, rather than pointlessly wasting it by fretting over that which we can't change. It is, in other words, an energy-saving technique. Energy is, of course, in very short supply when we are exhausted, so energy conservation is essential. In addition, acceptance will allow us to feel more at peace with ourselves and our circumstances.

Radical acceptance entails acknowledging both our inner and our outer realities. Let's start with the former. Self-acceptance means accepting the good and the bad, including our most undesirable traits and habits. It is only when we fully own our darker parts that we can begin to change in a meaningful way. The psychologist Carl Rogers observes the 'curious paradox' that 'when I accept myself as I am, then I change'.[4] One of the founding fathers of Cognitive Behavioural Therapy, Albert Ellis, was famously dismissive of the concept of self-esteem. Self-esteem, he felt, is always reliant on achievement and external approval and is linked to conceptions of success-bound value and worth. Instead, Ellis urges us to practise unconditional self-acceptance – warts and all. Self-acceptance, in Ellis's view, entails a fundamental and unshakeable respect for our personhood, whether or not we perform well, and whether or not other people approve of us and our behaviours. 'Unconditional acceptance', he argues, 'means liking yourself, others, and the world when you are not getting what you want and in spite of your getting what you don't want.'[5] Ellis urges us fully to accept ourselves as 'valuable and enjoyable humans' regardless of whether we are suc-cessful and productive and whether others approve of or love us.[6] That is, of course, much easier said than done. And it is hardest to practise self-acceptance when we are on our knees, unable to perform as we used to, feeling helpless and broken. But these moments are also a true litmus test.

Being human, taking risks and having skin in the game also entails that we will make errors and not always feel good. We will get hurt and we won't always succeed, even if we try our best. While we can direct and control our effort most of the time, we cannot control the outcomes of our striving. There are many obstacles out there, some of which are structural in nature, as well as competing agendas and desires. We can't change our past or predict our future. But if we let go of our 'woulds', 'coulds' and 'shoulds', we may be better able to tap more into an 'it is what it is' mindset.

It is also true that it can be harder than we think to know what is good or bad for us, as the Daoist parable of the farmer demonstrates. That farmer is a paragon of gracious acceptance. Crucially, he accepts both what seems initially positive and negative with equanimity, refusing to make rash judgements. In fact, he refuses to make any judgements at all:

Once upon a time in ancient China there was a farmer who owned a horse. 'You are so lucky!' his neighbours told him. 'You have a horse that can pull the cart for you.'

'Maybe', the farmer replied.

One day he forgot to close his gate and the horse

ran off. 'Poor you! This is terrible news!' his neighbours cried. 'Such bad luck!'

'Maybe', the farmer replied.

A couple of days later the horse returned, bringing with it six wild horses. 'How wonderful! You are the luckiest person ever', his neighbours told him. 'Now you are rich!'

'Maybe', the farmer replied.

The following week the farmer's son tried to break in one of the wild horses. It kicked out and broke his leg. 'Oh no!' the neighbours cried, 'such misfortune, all over again!'

'Maybe', the farmer replied.

The next day the Emperor's soldiers came to the village and took away all the young men to fight in the war. The farmer's son was left behind. 'You are so lucky!' his neighbours cried.

'Maybe', the farmer replied.[7]

The farmer wisely yields to whatever fate presents him with, neither rejoicing nor despairing over his circumstances. He offers no resistance to what happens to him because he knows that external events are beyond our control and will keep changing. What is more, we simply cannot know what will turn out to have been good or bad events in our lives.

Accepting what is, and letting go of what we think should be, is an essential pillar of Daoism. In its central text, the *Tao te ching* (c. fourth century BCE), the philosopher Lao-tzu advocates a mindset based on acceptance that is truly radical. In Daoism, acceptance centres on the idea of offering no resistance to the natural order of things. It is a form of yielding and going with the flow. Lao-tzu promotes a sophisticated form of submitting our will to cosmic forces by accepting what is and loosening our attachments to specific outcomes. He invites us to adopt a mindset of radical reconciliation with whatever life throws at us – not least because everything is in flux.

What we judge to be bad one moment may prove to have been good for us in the longer run. This is true of our state of exhaustion, too. For our exhaustion may compel us to listen to our body. It may lead us to change our lives, protect us from future harm, or else simply to give ourselves up to a period of rest and reflection.

B is for Burnout

The term 'burnout' emerged in the 1970s in the US. It quickly became a popular metaphor for mental and physical exhaustion caused by chronic stressors in the workplace. At first, burnout was thought to affect mainly people in helper professions – social workers, teachers, psychotherapists, counsellors, carers and nurses. People working in health and education tend to be driven by altruistic rather than materialist motives. And the higher our expectations, and the more we associate our professions with purpose and meaning, the greater our despair and suffering when reality bites. Being burnt out, thus understood, means we have become martyrs to our own high ideals. The writer Jonathan Malesic defines burnout as the experience of being pulled between expectations and reality at work. We burn out, he argues, not because we are exhausted but because our hearts are broken. Our love for work went unrequited – it did not love us back. And nor did it bring us the dignity, purpose and recognition for which we hoped. Burnout, he writes, is 'an ailment of the soul. We burn out in large part because we believe work is the sure path to social, moral, and spiritual flourishing.'[1]

The American social psychologist Christina Maslach provided the first tools for measuring burnout in the 1980s and also formulated its standard definition: 'Burnout is a syndrome of emotional exhaustion, depersonalisation, and reduced personal accomplishment that can occur among individuals who do "people work" of some kind.'[2] The symptoms of 'depersonalisation' can include a cynical, callous or indifferent attitude towards the people with whom we work – be they patients, students, customers, colleagues or clients.

In the late 1980s and 90s, burnout was gradually recognised as a serious occupational health condition that can occur in any sector. It was subsequently defined more broadly as 'a state of exhaustion in which one is cynical about the value of one's occupation and doubtful of one's capacity to perform'.[3] Alternatively, we can also look at burnout as a process, the gradual erosion of a positive state of mind. Burnout thus understood is a state in which our engagement wanes, in which 'energy turns into exhaustion, involvement turns into cynicism, and efficacy turns into ineffectiveness'.[4]

The key symptoms of burnout are exhaustion in the form of a deep kind of fatigue that isn't curable by resting. This state tends to be accompanied by a very negative assessment of the value of our work, and resentment of the people with whom we work and the organisations in which we are embedded. When we are burnt out, we may also experience brain fog and an inability to concentrate. We may suffer from insomnia or restlessness, we may drink too much, be prone to procrastinating and engage in endless displacement activities. We often become increasingly unable to do the work we are expected to do, and may feel a great sense of shame about our inability to perform as we used to. In cases of very serious burnout, we may even suffer a full-scale nervous breakdown and suddenly become completely unable to function at work and perhaps also in other areas of our lives.

Today, everyone is talking about burnout. This is partly because the popular consensus on what burnout is has become ever looser. It is a welcoming metaphor, allowing people to project all kinds of agendas onto the term. Recently, burnout statistics have gone through the roof.[5] What is going on? Why has burnout become so ubiquitous? Are we really more exhausted and depleted than ever before, or do we just talk about it more?

As mentioned in the introduction, Anne Helen Petersen draws attention to the complex structural conditions of burnout amongst millennials, showing that the dream of endless generational social mobility has come to a halt and that many of the work- and self-realization myths millennials were fed have turned to ash. Education and getting a college degree are no longer a route to a stable middle-class existence. Permanent employment with pensions and benefits and fairly compensated work is harder to secure than ever, as more and more jobs are outsourced to freelancers and associates. They battle with high student debts, unaffordable rents and limited opportunities. Millennials live in a state of permanent precarity, a feeling that everything they have ever worked for could just disappear. They have internalised very damaging attitudes to work and rest, basically feeling that they should be working all the time. All of this demands a high psychological toll. 'The burnout condition is more than just addiction to work', Petersen writes:

It's an alienation from the self, and from desire. If you subtract your ability to work, who are you? Is there a self left to excavate? Do you know what you like and don't like when there's no one there to watch, and no exhaustion to force you to choose the path of least resistance? Do you know how to move without always moving forward?[7]

There is no doubt that the twenty-first-century world of work entails unique psycho-social and economic stressors. Many of them are perfidious. The demands of neo-liberal competition and the growth imperative, which is based on maximising profit and optimising resource extraction at all costs, come at a price. As do email and social media, which make some things easier and many others much harder – and our constant availability means it is much more difficult to escape the things that cause us distress. While our attention spans have shrunk, our loneliness levels have increased. Because we are constantly connected and reachable, the boundaries between work and leisure have become more porous than ever, with work constantly bleeding into our mental, digital and physical spaces. Moreover, most of the tech we use at work and at home is designed to make us addicted to it, and new technology in particular has had a significant negative impact on our mental health. Finally, economic uncertainty and the threat of climate change, as well as pandemics and war, have made many of us feel very anxious. We are constantly exposed to upsetting news, and yet have very few practical means of taking action on the key issues of our day. Although our ancestors, too, struggled with exhaustion, there can be no doubt that we live in particularly fast-changing, complex and worrying times.

And yet, strange as it might seem, burnout is a diagnosis that also has positive connotations – like the 'fashionable diseases' of the past, melancholia and neurasthenia, a nineteenth-century forerunner of burnout that was based on the notion of nervous weakness. Melancholia was firmly aligned with creativity, scholarship and genius, while neurasthenia was associated with brain work, sensitivity and an artistic constitution. Burnout is, in part at least, a similarly heroic diagnosis, worn by some as a badge of honour. Being burnt out signifies that we have given everything, and more, to work. The burnt out literally take work deadly seriously. They are in constant demand, highly important and extremely conscientious. They care. They take on responsibility – more than they can carry. They always help out. They are not shirkers. They are not losers. In fact, research suggests that a very large percentage of the burnt out are former winners and high-flyers.[8]

This does not mean that I wish to diminish the suffering we feel when we burn out. Nor is being in that state in any way a cakewalk. It is not. For many of my clients, burnout is an existential threat, forcing them completely to re-evaluate their lives, and often to abandon the careers for which they spent years preparing. What makes burnout so dangerous is that it traps us in a no-man's land where we can neither work nor allow ourselves to rest. Many of us feel tremendous shame and guilt about burning out – very much the opposite of feeling heroic. My point is simply that burnout is a diagnosis that comes with some cultural validation and even status. It bears, for example, less stigma than depression and other mental health conditions. And this is the case because our culture validates work, and working hard, and, to a certain extent at least, looks kindly on those who are wounded in the battlefield of work. Being burnt out also means to be a victim of the values of our age. And there is some solace and community to be found in that.

But what can we actually do when we are burnt out? How can we heal? I continue to be struck by the paradox that looms so large at the heart of the debates: the happiness industry pushes individual coping strategies, while research shows that in the vast majority of cases, it is our working environments that are making us sick. The burnout researchers Christina Maslach and Michael P. Leiter identify six main factors causing burnout in organisations: excessive workload, insufficient autonomy, inadequate rewards, breakdown of community, mismatch of values and unfairness.[9] When we experience any of these at work, we are much more likely to burn out. A growing number of healthcare professionals argue that burnout should be reconceived as 'moral injury', that it is a result of unbridgeable value clashes, ethical dilemmas and continuous violations of our dignity at work.[10]

The World Health Organization clearly defines burnout as an occupational health condition, not a mental health issue. But even the WHO's definition of burnout is troubled by what I call the 'burnout paradox': 'Burnout is a syndrome conceptualized as resulting from chronic workplace stress that has not been successfully managed.'[11] This sounds accusatory, putting the onus on the sufferer, blaming, in essence, the burnt out for their bad stress management skills. What might 'successful management' of chronic stress even look like? There is an undeniable tension between conceptions of the role of external structures and personal agency. What can we really do, then, to counteract occupational burnout, other than leaving our jobs or radically reforming our workplaces – both of which are not realistic options in most cases? It is, first and foremost, the organisations that cause their staff to burn out that need coaching and training, not their burnt out employees.

When in the grips of burnout, then, we need to be very discerning about what is and what isn't our personal responsibility. Part of what makes burnout so intractable and difficult to treat is precisely that it is mostly a result of structural forces. But that insight alone can be healing: by recognising the social factors of burnout that aren't our fault, rather than seeing it as an inherent failure of our own (or as a badge of honour), we can begin to take back some power for ourselves.

C is for Capitalism

Let us begin with a little parable. You may have encountered it before:

An American investment banker went on a much-needed holiday to Thailand. Having worked hard all year, he was exhausted and dying for a proper break. He booked himself into a luxury hotel, drank cocktails at the bar in the evenings, and spent his days fishing in the calm emerald-green waters that caressed the edges of the resort's sandy beach and gently rocked the colourful small boats moored at the ramshackle pier of a nearby fishing village. On his first afternoon, the banker struck a deal with one of the local fishermen, who sat idly on the pier in the sunshine. He agreed to take the banker to a good fishing spot in his little boat for a few hours each day. On the third day, as he sat in the boat fishing, the banker began to question the fisherman about his life.

'How many fish do you catch on a good day?' he asked.

'I never catch more than five.'

'Why?' the banker asked, astounded. He had already been able to catch seven on his second day, and was hoping to break his record the following day.

'Why not?' the fisherman replied. 'We only need

five. My family and I, we couldn't eat more than that, and fish doesn't keep.'

'Why don't you sell the additional ones at the market, or to the hotel?'

'Why should I?' the fisherman shrugged.

'To make a profit, of course! In just a few weeks, you could earn enough to buy a second boat, and recruit an employee. Together you could catch even more fish and earn even more money. You could soon afford an entire flotilla of boats, build warehouses for storage and sell your fish at markets that are further away.'

'But why would I want to do this?' The fisherman was genuinely puzzled.

'You would grow rich!'

'And then? What would I do with my money?'

The banker laughed. He thought the fisherman was pulling his leg. But when the latter remained silent, the banker tried to explain further: 'You could buy Porsches, live in a big house with air-conditioning and a pool, wear fancy clothes, buy the latest tech. You could drink champagne instead of water. You could eat oysters every day. You could buy your wife designer handbags and Manolo Blahniks. You could send your children to Harvard!'

The fisherman was unimpressed. These things did not mean anything to him.

The banker started to become flustered. But then he had an idea: 'You could go on holidays to great places like this one, and spend all day enjoying the sun and fishing!'

'But I'm already doing that', the fisherman said, smiling, and then he rowed the banker back to the shore.

The tale is in itself a Rorschach test of some kind. Depending on how we look at it, we will arrive at very different conclusions. Those of us who have fully internalised the capitalist mandate constantly to multiply our assets will see the fisherman's stance as an illustration of stupidity, laziness and lost opportunities. But those who are tired of living to work rather than working to live may see the fisherman's point. Wherever we stand, the parable poses some profound questions: What is the right balance between time spent earning and time spent living? Between doing and being, striving and enjoying, ambition and contentment, rest and work? How much do we need to be happy, and is the price we pay for our luxuries and comforts (measured in life-cost) really worth its rewards? And what, ultimately, is the purpose of life?

For most of us, it is hard not to think like the investment banker, trapped, as we are, in the 'iron cage' of the capitalist mindset. Economic traditionalists like the fisherman probably inspire and horrify us in equal measure. Their values are at the opposite end of the spectrum to ours: They are not interested in maximising their profits, only in covering their basic needs. Their concern is with the present rather than the future. Consequently, they are more interested in working less than in earning more. They value pleasure more highly than achievement. They are grateful for what they have rather than constantly dreaming of more.

C is for Capitalism

While we may find it hard to think outside the capitalist paradigm, it is worth remembering that, historically speaking, the capitalist mode of being is still young. The rhythm of work changed only in the nineteenth century, with the onset of industrialisation. Before then, our patterns of work and rest were collective, dominated by nature, the seasons, holy days and the vagaries of the weather. Hunter-gatherer societies spent even more time resting than agricultural ones. We were not constantly servicing machines, or else being subtly manipulated by algorithms that are already much smarter than us. And while we cannot yet imagine any other viable models of organising our societies and economies, it is nevertheless likely that capitalism will not be with us forever. My wish for the future is that our children's children will look back at our system as primitive.

My broader point here is that our exhaustion is not just caused by inner noise and toxic working environments. It is also bound up with deeper cultural attitudes towards work and rest. One of the most important texts on that topic is *The Protestant Ethic and the Spirit of Capitalism* (1904–05), by the founding father of sociology, Max Weber.[1] In his famous essay, Weber establishes a parallel between the Protestant religious ethos and what he calls the 'spirit' of capitalism. Weber asks why it was that being efficient and successful in our chosen profession became akin to a sacred duty. It is no doubt true that, today, our jobs are as important in defining who we are as are our racial and class origins and our gender. 'What do you do?' is one of the first questions we ask when we meet someone.

Moreover, the aspiration to do well at work, and gradually to rise through the ranks of our chosen profession, is an aim that many of us accept without even thinking about it. Work is now so firmly enmeshed with our identities that it is a thing of existential importance, not just an economic necessity or a means to an end. For many of us, work is God. Or at least it is the lodestar in our life, tied up with purpose, meaning, status and even spiritual flourishing.

Weber notes the closeness of the German words *Beruf* (profession) and *Berufung* (calling). He also observes that Protestants don't just work hard, but, being (as he says) rather dour and joyless in spirit, do not tend to spend what they earn. In other words, they are ideal little capitalists because they save and reinvest rather than squandering their money on pleasurable things. But why do they bother to work so hard if fun is not part of the equation?

Weber explains this puzzling phenomenon through recourse to the importance of asceticism in the Protestant religion. Protestant reformers such as Martin Luther, John Calvin and John Knox wished to limit the roles of intermediaries between believers and God. They successfully abolished Catholic rituals such as confession and indulgences, which required priests to act as middlemen. But that also caused problems. Because sinful behaviour could no longer simply be forgiven in the confessional, Protestants needed a different kind of reassurance about their state of grace. This is where the importance of asceticism and worldly success came in. Success in one's profession became the external sign that was thought to signal a state of grace. In plainer words, Protestants believed that doing well in their jobs was a clear indication that they were one of the elect.

Let's not even try to unravel the many paradoxes in this chain of beliefs: religion is not a thing of logic. What matters here for us is that industriousness, efficiency, discipline and a strong sense of personal responsibility became essential parts of the Protestant moral code. The fetishisation of productivity as an earthly sign of grace also explains the condemnation of its opposites – above all, comfort, laziness, sensual pleasure, waste and rest.[2] As Weber puts it: 'Not leisure and enjoyment, but *only activity* serves to increase the glory of God, according to the definite manifestations of His will.' He specifies further:

> *Waste of time* is thus the first and in principle the deadliest of sins. The span of human life is infinitely short and precious in order to reassure oneself of one's calling. Loss of time through sociability, 'idle talk', luxury, even more sleep than is necessary for health – six to at most eight hours – is worthy of absolute moral condemnation.[3]

Here, we can see clearly how it came to pass that slacking and lack of productivity became the key secular sins of the capitalist age. The squandering of time and energy was considered as scandalous an act as the squandering of money itself.

Capitalism has now spread from Western, mainly Protestant cultures to most other parts of the world. While most of us may no longer be religious, we are still significantly shaped by the moral code of our forebears. But there is hope. If we do not automatically accept the dominant beliefs and values of our culture, but turn them into the object of our critical attention, we can decide more freely which codes we wish to live by. And we can begin to be inspired by those who make radically different choices – like the Southeast Asian fisherman.

D is for Dante

What has Dante got to do with exhaustion, you may wonder? The Italian poet is most famous for having written *The Divine Comedy* (1308–21). This epic poem has been described as an extended revenge fantasy, because in it, Dante clearly relishes describing, in great detail, a plethora of ghastly punishments for his many enemies and rivals. The poem chronicles Dante's alter ego's journey from Hell to Paradise, where he is eventually reunited with Beatrice – the love of his life who died young. Dante is led through Inferno and Purgatory by a wise guide, the Roman poet Virgil. In the course of their travels, the two encounter a wide array of sinners who are served tailor-made punishments for their vices. The reason why Dante made it into this *A–Z*, however, is this: his journey from dark to light can also be read as a depiction of the gradual overcoming of his spiritual and physical weariness. There are numerous references in the text to exhaustion, acedia (a theological version of melancholia that gradually morphed into the sin of sloth), tiredness, sleepiness, lack of energy and spiritual apathy. And amongst the sinners who receive the cruellest punishments are the slothful and the lukewarm.

When he starts his epic journey early in the spring of the year 1300, Dante is 35 years old. In the middle of life's path, he famously finds himself lost and alone in a dark forest. He has lost his way both literally and metaphorically: he is full of doubts, his faith is weak, political chaos reigns in his hometown of Florence and he is not properly honouring the memory of his beloved Beatrice. More importantly, the Dante we encounter in the opening cantos of *Inferno* is not only spiritually lost but also lacking in energy. On his descent into Hell, he is constantly overcome by moments of severe exhaustion. He frequently collapses 'as one with sudden slumber seiz'd'.[1] We learn that he 'Such sleepy dullness in that instant weigh'd /My senses down, when the true path I left'.[2] He repeatedly has to let his tired body rest, and bemoans his 'difficult short breath / Forespent with toiling'.[3] But as his teacher Virgil's benign influence grows, Dante's state slowly changes. The closer he comes to Paradise, the higher his energy levels become. Eventually, he sheds both his physical sluggishness and his spiritual apathy like an old skin. But how does he do it? And what can we learn from him?

First and foremost, Dante is made to witness the terrible consequences of sinful behaviour – including the sin of sloth. Sloth, you may remember, is one of the ancient big seven. It features in the list of the Seven Deadly Sins because it wasn't primarily understood as physical laziness, but rather as a bad mental attitude – a lack of faith in God and a weak commitment to his glorious creation. The slothful were proud and ungrateful, lacking in appreciation. The *Inferno* and *Purgatory* parts of *The Divine Comedy* are classic cautionary tales: this is the fate that awaits you too, dear reader, if you do not change your ways,

Dante suggests. And while inducing fear and terror and threatening punishment to stimulate behavioural change is not a subtle strategy, it can be effective. It certainly appears to be so in Dante's case.

The many sinners Dante encounters are punished according to the law of *contrapasso*, which means that sins are admonished by tortures that are carefully matched to the vice in question. Flatterers, for example, are immersed in excrement. The greedy are tied to the ground, their hands and feet bound, because they were too attached to earthly material goods. In the fifth circle of Hell, Dante and his guide encounter the sullen. The sullen are stuck in the muddy waters of the river Styx, forced to swallow slime. Virgil explains:

Fix'd in the slime they say: 'Sad once were we
In the sweet air made gladsome by the sun,
Carrying a foul and lazy mist within:
Now in these murky settlings are we sad.'[4]

The sin of the sullen is that they were sorrowful without cause, sad in the sunshine, not appreciating God's gifts. In other words, they lacked gratitude. Later, Dante also encounters the slothful. They are compelled to run around without respite, their punishment being endless activity, to counter the lack of activity in their earthly life. The slothful who rush past Dante and his guide are wild and frenzied, forever deprived of the rest they cherished so much when they were alive. A crowd of repentant idlers are condemned to eternal fervour and business, to compensate for the sloth, negligence and half-heartedness they showed in their lifetime. They are so anxious to advance that they cannot even stop to chat with Dante.

Importantly, Dante's own cardinal sin, too, is sloth. Virgil repeatedly reprimands his utterly exhausted charge for his lack of energy. He sternly warns him to cast aside his laziness, for he who spends his life resting cannot come to fame. The lazy will leave no trace on this earth, having squandered their life span. They will not have anything to show for, no kind of legacy, and their memory will dissipate like foam on water. 'Therefore rise', Virgil urges Dante: 'vanish thy weariness / By the mind's effort, in each struggle form'd'.[5] Here and elsewhere in the poem, exhaustion and tepidity are represented as a grave and dangerous spiritual failing. Virgil declares that the right attitude and resolve can overcome the limitations and weaknesses of the flesh. The spirit, he holds, can always defeat the body's torpor.

Dante and Virgil also meet Belacqua, a man who cannot climb Mount Purgatory, and will therefore never reach a state of salvation. Belacqua spends his days lounging languidly in the shade behind a boulder at the foot of the mountain. He is listless, exhausted, sitting with his arms around his knees, his head bowed. Dante notes the slowness of his movements, the brevity of his speech and the fact that he lifts his eyes just high enough to be able to see his visitors. Belacqua explains that he cannot muster the energy to climb Mount Purgatory, shunning the effort that would be required to achieve redemption. He thinks the attempt would be pointless, because he lacks the hope that his journey would be successful. He has given up without even trying.

Belacqua's predicament shows why chronic exhaustion is so self-perpetuating and difficult to overcome: to be able to take the first steps towards changing our condition, we need to have faith that we stand a chance at succeeding. However, when we are exhausted, faith and optimism are among the first things to go. Hopelessness is a key symptom in most exhaustion-related states. We often find it impossible to imagine that we will ever feel different again.

Dante, however, has a motivational guide. Under Virgil's wise mentorship, he steadily advances towards Paradise, and is gradually purged of his own sins. As the sins fall off him, his step becomes lighter and more energetic. Eventually he asks his Master: 'Say, master, of what heavy thing have I / Been lighten'd, that scarce aught the sense of toil / Affects me journeying?' Virgil tells Dante that, purged from his sins, his feet will, 'by heartiness of will / Be so o'ercome, they not alone shall feel / No sense of labour, but delight much more / Shall wait them urg'd along their upward way'.[6] The metaphorical gravity of sin weighs down not just Dante's spiritual but also his physical body.

Physical and spiritual exhaustion in *The Divine Comedy*, then, are overcome in four steps: 1) by the threat of punishment; 2) by purification from sin; 3) by regaining faith and optimism; and finally, it is important to note point 4): Dante didn't do it on his own – he would never have succeeded without his personal coach and spiritual guide by his side. And while most of us will not consider our exhaustion to be a sinful state, and will also not be so easily scared into changing our ways by gory visions of punishments in the afterlife, there are nevertheless some lessons we can learn from *The Divine Comedy*.

First of all, we can contemplate what may happen if we do not change our work–life balance in this life of ours, here on earth. Above all, exhaustion is a warning sign, telling us that our lifestyle is not sustainable. What might be the long-term costs of ignoring this message? What do we risk losing, and is it worth the short-term gains? If we continue as we do, where will we be, say in five years from now? Will we, too, find ourselves lost and alone in the dark woods of our psyche?

Secondly, what are the many 'sins', small and major, that weigh us down – all the unhelpful habits and injurious rituals that contribute to our exhaustion? How might we purge them and lighten our steps? And what of the guilt and shame we carry around with us?

Thirdly, in what areas of our lives does our hopelessness and negative thinking prevent us from taking positive action? When are we Belacquas, cowering in the shade, our heads between our knees, thinking we would fail anyway, so what's the point in even trying? When we don't even try, we forsake our chance maybe not of salvation as such, but at least of changing our current state into a better one. I have always found Belacqua a particularly poignant and tragic figure – he is so close, literally only a short climb away from the doors of heaven, and yet he doesn't give himself a chance. And at the same time it is unclear whether he even could, whether he is truly a helpless victim of his condition or really just lacking in commitment and willpower. Could he even be the master of his own fate?

And last but not least, think about who could be your own Virgil, guiding you from darkness into light. It could be a friend or a good therapist or a coach. It is fine to ask for help when we are lost.

E is for Energy

Exhaustion's opposites include states of vitality, engagement, aliveness, vigour and strength. All of them are
marked by an abundance, even a bubbly surplus, of energy.
Vitality means that we have enough, and more, energy to
expend, including on extravagant, deliberately wasteful
and simply fun things. When we are exhausted, by contrast, we are trapped in a scarcity mindset. We anxiously
watch every tiny morsel of our energy, wondering whether
we can afford this activity or that. We dread wasting energy
on what is non-essential and live in constant fear of its
permanent depletion. But what exactly is human energy?
How can we imagine and measure it? And how can we
replenish it when we have none left – not even for restorative activities?

In spite of its importance, human energy remains a
curiously nebulous concept in the West. Energy is mainly
defined by describing what happens when it is absent.
Western medicine has analysed various syndromes that
are marked by a scarcity or even complete absence of
human energy, such as depression, chronic fatigue and
burnout. But apart from the prosaic calorie model used
in nutritional science, there is no broadly accepted model
of human energy in Western culture. Even in the psychoanalytical tradition, Freud and his successors' theories of

libido and drive energy remain strikingly elusive on closer inspection.

Many Eastern cultures, by contrast, have widely accepted models of human energy. There are, for example, the chakras and *prana* in the Indian tradition and *qi* in Traditional Chinese Medicine (TCM). Prana (the Sanskrit word for 'life force') is a core concept in many Hindu philosophical texts, such as the Upanishads and the Vedas. It is also central in various yoga traditions. In indigenous Central and Latin American shamanic cultures, moreover, many rituals centre on cleaning auras and unblocking energy fields, for example with the help of medicinal plants such as ayahuasca. In the West, more explicit concepts of human or life energy can only be found in the pre-modern era. The Greek physician Galen, for example, wrote about the 'animal spirits' (*pneuma psychikon* in Greek and *spiritus animalis* in Latin). In the early modern period, thinkers from the vitalist tradition theorised the idea of the *élan vital* – the 'vital spark' that differentiates animate from inanimate objects. But the tradition of recognised models of human energy ends with Freud's notion of libido.

Although references to human energy are ubiquitous in popular and medical debates, the concept remains vague. Why is that the case? Why has the discussion of human energy been relegated to the realms of the esoteric and pseudoscientific in modern Western culture? The fact that ours is the age of scientific materialism in which only what is measurable counts as real has certainly not helped. With the advent of evidence-based medicine, holistic conceptions of the mind–body nexus have fallen from favour.

But some of them are currently experiencing a revival, as Western medicine becomes ever more aware of its blind spots.

While coffee, sugar, alcohol and amphetamines can temporarily up our energy levels, they don't solve anything in the long run. In fact, our quick-fix schemes often make things worse. Many Asian techniques, by contrast, are designed to ensure long-term sustainability in our energy economies. TCM, for example, places a huge importance on preventative measures in the form of daily energy self-care rituals. In *The Yellow Emperor's Classic of Medicine* (c. 300–100 BCE), the primary source of Chinese medical theory, we find a justification for this approach:

> In the old days the sages treated disease by preventing illness before it began, just as a good government or emperor was able to take the necessary steps to avert war. Treating an illness after it has begun is like suppressing revolt after it has broken out. If someone digs a well when thirsty, or forges weapons after becoming engaged in battle, one cannot help but ask: Are not these actions too late?[1]

What can we learn from these ancient conceptions of energy, and of energy self-care? Some of us may already have experienced the beneficial powers of practices such as acupuncture, qi gong and yoga. Energy audits are another good starting point for learning to care for our energy in a more sustainable way. They can help us understand what drains our energy and what restores it. Which activities or people are energy-vampires that suck all life out of us? How can we recharge? What truly vitalises us? Just creating a list of these things can help us better understand the patterns of our energy movements.

We also need to relearn to pay more attention to our energy. By that I mean feeling more deeply into its rhythms. Energy rises and wanes like the sea, and its flow is determined by the complex interplay of internal and external factors. I'm always struck anew by how strongly my energy levels are influenced by my thoughts and emotions. A lovely chance encounter, a message from a friend, the unexpected sight of a heron by the river flowing past our house, or simply good news can propel me from a slumped, sunken state into one of lightness in seconds. By contrast, a work email that announces tasks I have to but really don't want to do, or having to see people I don't want to see can deplete me completely and make me feel deadly tired.

My eight-year-old daughter is even more extreme. Engaged and interested, she cannot stop talking and jumping around. She races rather than walks. But when she has to do homework or tidy her room, listen to conversations she deems boring, or go somewhere she doesn't want to go, she wilts like a cut flower. She can barely hold her head up. She yawns like a little animal about to go into hibernation, constantly rubs her eyes and suddenly seems dangerously anaemic. Anyone who doesn't believe in the mind–body nexus should study children.

But while desire, interest and optimism are vital factors in determining our energy levels, a permanent lack of energy can also have undiagnosed physical origins. It can be caused by illness, bad lifestyle choices or internal psychological stressors. Some research suggests that our baseline energy levels are biologically predetermined, and that some people simply have more energy at their disposal than others. Moreover, the question of human energy is also a broader biopolitical concern. An exhausted and disengaged workforce poses a potentially serious economic problem. Most companies have long realised that the enhancement of their staff's energy levels is in their interest and are therefore happy to invest in various well-being initiatives.

In physics, energy is something acting or moving that does work of some kind. It is one of the many tragedies of being human that the foundational principle in physics, the law of the conservation of energy, which states that energy can neither be created nor destroyed, but only converted from one form of energy to another, does not apply to us. In fact, the opposite is the case. Our physical energies are, from our mid-twenties onwards, perpetually on the wane, growing ever weaker, eventually dissipating into thin air.

Energy in the sciences can be expressed in neat formulas. It can be quantified and measured, and its behaviour can be described in laws. No such thing is possible when it comes to human energy. We can only, if at all, measure the effects of human energy, or else the effects of its absence. If we want to explore the question of energy from a different perspective, we have to turn to traditional or ancient wisdom, or else resort to metaphors. We may be full of beans, in high spirits, light-hearted, sparkling and buzzing with energy one day, and feel heavy, hollow, extinguished, shattered, sapped and spent the next. But maybe the fact that we have to make do with imagery when it comes to energy is not such a bad thing.

We may even wish to come up with our own: How do you envisage and experience your energy? Does it have a shape, a name, a colour? Is it a ball, a light, a rush of particles? Does it flow, throb, fizz, tug or stagnate? Where exactly can you feel it in your body? Do you think of your energy as primarily a matter of the will, the flesh, the psyche or the spirit? And how will you commit to care for it – today and in the future?

F is for Failure

Samuel Beckett's words, 'Ever tried. Ever failed. No matter. Try again. Fail again. Fail better', have become a popular cliché both in business management and in the literature on personal development.[1] And yet most of us don't know how to fail. That is because there is nothing harder than failing, let alone failing well. Failure is one of our most deep-seated fears. To try our best and not succeed can be the cause of great shame and anguish. And, of course, of a deep kind of existential exhaustion that is caused by the loss of motivation and hope. Often, our self-worth is firmly tied to our successes in the arenas of work, play or love. If the activities to which we dedicate our time and effort don't work out as we wish, we tend to suffer two blows: loss of status and dignity in the external world, and injuries to our self-image. Failure threatens both our pride and our sense of accomplishment.

Failure, then, often feels like a matter of existential importance, irrespective of whether it is in our career or our personal relationships. In highly competitive individualist societies, it is particularly stigmatised. Donald Trump, for example, was obsessed with calling people losers. In his books, being a loser was the worst thing anyone could be – worse than being uncaring, a liar, amoral or even a criminal. The Trumpian loser is supposedly someone who either loses their money and power or else squanders opportunities for maximising them. Losers are too weak to succeed in a society in which the strongest and smartest, or, more accurately, the most ruthless, thrive. Trump is far from being alone in this assessment. This vilification of the 'loser' is very much part of our culture. At a deeper level, this cultural attitude is indicative of more timeless anxieties about the transient nature of our power and possessions, and about helplessness and dependency.

How, then, can we practise what Beckett preached? How can we fail better? Failing well can only be achieved on two conditions: acceptance and learning. Let's begin with acceptance. Statistically speaking, it is highly likely that we will fail on numerous fronts in our lives. More than 50 per cent of marriages in the West end in divorce. Long-term relationships are now harder than ever to form and to sustain. Globally, an estimated 90 per cent of new start-ups fail. In the UK, almost one in five new businesses goes into administration in its first year. Many of our transactional dynamics now have the quality of zero-sum games, where there are clearly defined winners and losers, one player's gain being equivalent to another player's loss. And yet we are all in thrall to survivorship bias: our attention is firmly focused on winners, the small percentage of highly successful people, products or businesses who made it through arduous selection processes.

Generally speaking, the more courageous we are and the more we put ourselves out there, the higher our chances of failing become. Failure is a natural consequence of taking risks, and risks are an inevitable part of being human.

We risk rejection whenever we ask someone out. We risk having our hearts broken when we form relationships of any kind, be they with friends or with lovers. When we speak our minds, when we present ourselves authentically to the world, we risk offending others. We risk losing our time and money when we launch businesses, invent products or change careers to pursue our passions. Whenever we engage in competitive activities such as sports or games, we risk losing to people who are more talented or experienced than us. When we pour our hearts and souls into novels, music or art, we risk people not appreciating what we cherish. And yet shirking risks of those kinds is simply not an option, for risk avoidance is nothing less than life avoidance.

A sensible attitude to failure would not simply entail accepting that failure is very likely to be a constant companion in our lives, but also acknowledging the fact that failure is the flip-side of care: anything that is worth doing, having or being entails risk. The more we care about the outcome, the higher the stakes are, of course. While we cannot and should not take risks all the time, we also cannot seek to eliminate all risk from our lives because that would also mean eliminating everything about which we care and that might make us happy. The risk-avoidant approach may result in us denying ourselves the chance to meet our most basic needs. Those needs include forming and maintaining nourishing relationships, seeking knowledge and new experiences, striving for status and practising altruism.

Theodore Roosevelt was right when he said: 'It is hard to fail, but it is worse never to have tried to succeed.' The worst kind of failure is not even trying because of our fear of failure. In fact, this is one of the most serious existential crimes we can commit, and we ourselves are its victims. If we were able to develop a kinder and more compassionate attitude to failure, if we could cease to be our own harshest judges, we could significantly lower the stakes and disentangle failure from our worth as human beings.

While we cannot control whether or not we succeed, we can control how we view ourselves afterwards. What would we dare to attempt in life if we could genuinely allow ourselves to fail? The writer Maya Angelou notes: 'You see, we may encounter many defeats, but we must not be defeated. It may even be necessary to encounter the defeat, so that we can know who we are. So that we can see, oh, that happened, and I rose. I did get knocked down flat in front of the whole world, and I rose. I didn't run away – I rose right where I'd been knocked down.'[2] In other words, the more we fail, the stronger we will become and the faster we will learn to rise again.

It is also worth interrogating what we mean by failure. At a basic level, failure is of course the opposite of success, not getting what we want or what we set out to achieve. But there are very different ways of looking at setbacks of that kind. First, they may be temporary in nature. We may, for example, have lost a single battle but still stand a chance of winning the war. As Winston Churchill put it: 'Success is not final, failure is not fatal: it is the courage to continue that counts.' In less militaristic terms, sometimes our failures may only be temporary setbacks on a longer journey towards a cause that will ultimately succeed. It is no coincidence that many fairy tales involve characters who must attempt something three times before they are successful.

Most importantly, however, failures are our most valuable teachers. Our failures can show us how to get better, grow and learn from our experiences, including the shameful and painful ones. Thomas Edison, the inventor of the lightbulb, is famous for having stated: 'I have not failed. I've just found 10,000 ways that won't work.' Inventors and scientists are particularly adept at learning from failure. They patiently try out and methodically assess what doesn't work, until they eventually find a way that does. Most of us won't fall into that category, for it is challenging to look at our problems through an experimental lens. And yet we have important lessons to learn from the domains in which failures are the objects of analytical study.

The journalist Matthew Syed has written an entire book about the art of learning from failure. In *Black Box Thinking: Marginal Gains and the Secrets of High Performance* (2015), he presents a compelling case for changing our collective attitudes to failure. When we fail, most of us feel shame, blame others or simply try to hide our mistakes. But that, Syed argues, is completely to misunderstand how progress is made: without engaging seriously with failure, there would be no science, no development, no growth. He goes on to advocate what he calls 'black box thinking', a dramatic change in our mindset that destigmatises failure and instead seeks to harness its benefits. As he observes, an exemplary attitude to failure already exists in the aviation industry. After each plane crash, considerable effort is invested in the retrieval and analysis of the information contained in the 'black box' flight recorder in order to understand what went wrong and to feed that knowledge back into the production process. It is one of the reasons that air travel is, statistically speaking, one of the safest forms of travel there is.

Syed argues that the opposite mindset prevails in the healthcare sector, where no productive procedures are in place to learn from error. This is astounding, for the rate of deaths from preventable human errors is staggeringly high. About 100,000 Americans die of avoidable human medical errors each year. This is 'the equivalent of two jumbo jets falling out of the sky every twenty-four hours'. Lagging behind only heart disease and cancer, preventable medical error is currently the third biggest killer in the US. In the UK, it is estimated that one in every ten patients 'is killed or injured as a consequence of medical or institutional shortcomings'.[3] In France, the number is even higher, an estimated 14 per cent. The core difference between the healthcare and aviation sectors is the attitude to failure. Where failures are examined openly and analytically, without blame or denial, and when feedback is acted upon, growth and improvement follow naturally. In institutional cultures where cover-ups and non-transparency are standard, by contrast, blame and shame prevail.

Our reluctance to learn from failure is not, however, due only to dominant working cultures. Psychological reasons also play an important role. Chief among them is our inclination to avoid, if necessary at high cost, what the social psychologist Leon Festinger has called 'cognitive dissonance'. Festinger argues that we have a very strong drive to establish harmony between our values, beliefs, behaviours and external information. If we perceive an inconsistency between our beliefs and external evidence, we strive to eliminate this dissonance. Because it is the path of least resistance, however, we tend not to change our deeply-held beliefs, but rather to ignore or reframe evidence that does not fit into our picture of the world. Because cognitive dissonance threatens our inner balance and self-esteem, we often filter, twist and bend what disturbs us.

The attempt to avoid cognitive dissonance may, of course, also include our own shortcomings. We can invest considerable mental energy in blocking mistakes we have made from entering our conscious thought, spinning self-justifications and alternative narratives, or else putting the blame on others. When it comes to developing a healthier attitude to failing, then, the cultural and psychological odds are against us. Nevertheless, we may begin to look at failure differently, as an essential part of lives lived courageously. In addition, we may wish to peer into our own black boxes from time to time, especially after we crash, and see what kind of information awaits us there. The poet Antonio Machado urges us simply to harvest wisdom from our past failures:

Last night, as I was sleeping,
I dreamt – marvelous error! –
that I had a beehive
here inside my heart.

F is for Failure

And the golden bees
were making white combs
and sweet honey
from my old failures ...[4]

G is for Ghosts

Sometimes, being caught in a bad situation can drain us of all vitality, even destroy our will to live. When we are that unlucky, we turn into ghosts, neither fully alive nor dead. We may continue to function at a physical level, but our spirits appear to have departed. Empty shells, we are incapable of experiencing joy. In fact, more often than not, we don't feel anything at all. We have numbed our feelings to such an extent that we don't even register the true scale of our suffering. And this is the point, of course: because it would be too devastating to hear what our feelings have to tell us, it is safer not to feel anything at all. How big is this army of the uncomfortably numb? How many of us are frozen on the inside, reduced by soul-destroying work to shadowy traces of our former selves?

Perhaps the most famous ghost-worker of that kind is described in Herman Melville's short story 'Bartleby, the Scrivener: A Story of Wall Street' (1853).[1] The story opens with the narrator informing us that he has employed a man called Bartleby as an additional law copyist. The narrator is a conflict-shy solicitor who, for years, has put up with two copyists who are insolent and dysfunctional, but whose weaknesses balance each other out. The solicitor's offices are 'deficient in what landscape painters call "life"': all windows look out onto shafts, brick walls and dead ends.[2] Into this deathly environment wanders Bartleby, 'pallidly neat, pitiably respectable, incurably forlorn!'[3] He is placed at a desk facing a viewless window with very little light.

At first, Bartleby copies assiduously, but refuses to perform any tasks beyond copying. Whenever the narrator asks him to help with something else, Bartleby responds mildly: 'I would prefer not to.' This becomes his trademark phrase. In fact, he says little else throughout the story. Gradually, he prefers not to do ever more things and, eventually, he informs the narrator that he has given up copying, too. Having ceased to perform any work tasks at all, Bartleby henceforth spends his days in 'dead-wall reveries', gazing dull-eyed at the 'dead brick wall' onto which his window looks.[4]

The narrator decides to let Bartleby go. But Bartleby prefers not to quit the premises, in which he now also lives full-time. His ghostly presence in the offices is increasingly disconcerting. In keeping with his gutless management style, the narrator eventually decides to move his practice elsewhere. Yet even after the narrator has moved out, Bartleby refuses to budge. When he is forcibly removed by the new tenants, he continues to haunt the landing and stairwells of the building – like a ghost that can't leave the location where they were murdered, hoping for an act of restitution, a restoration of justice that will stem the bleeding spiritual wound. But Bartleby is carried off to the 'Tombs', the local jail, where he stops eating and gradually wastes away. The narrator tries to alleviate his bad conscience by visiting his gentle nemesis and by paying a 'grub man' to feed him. But when he calls on him a second time he finds Bartleby dead, rolled up in a foetal position in front of one of the prison walls. 'Huddled at the base of the wall, his knees drawn up, and lying on his side, his head touching the cold stones', Bartleby has finally succeeded in wasting away.[5]

Bartleby is described as 'motionless', 'mild' and 'cadaverous', and his ghost-like paleness is repeatedly emphasised.[6] He is dead in life, devoid of any desires, defined only negatively by what he would 'prefer not to' do. He never speaks but to answer. Nowadays, we would probably describe him as burnt out and anhedonic – unable to experience pleasure of any kind. Lonely, isolated and alienated, he declines to take an interest in anything and also refuses to accept help. When the narrator discusses possible alternative jobs with him, Bartleby dismisses all of them, despite his assertion that he is not particular. In that sense, he is a bit like the protagonist in Kafka's short story 'A Hunger Artist', who starves himself to death but claims that he would happily eat if only he could find a food he likes.

Bartleby starts out as a fully-functioning, polite and pro-ductive worker. But soon, his dull and oppressive working environment saps all the life out of him. The repetitive, mindless task of copying, the windowless office and the horrid colleagues, as well as his hypocritical boss, contrib-ute further to his rapid decline. Marxist critics have argued that it is the monotonous, creativity-killing and soul-de-stroying labour that lead to Bartleby's deterioration. It is also significant that the law offices in which his health deteriorates are situated on Wall Street – the symbolic centre of capitalism. Others, however, consider Bartleby's grand refusal as an act of heroic resistance against the productivity dictate – the injunction to be industrious at all times. We may see Bartleby as a rebel who protests against an early version of burnout culture. Others still have interpreted Bartleby's exhaustion and subsequent breakdown as essentially spiritual in nature, as a reaction to the empty materialism of our soulless age.

The story is also an illustration of the dangers that toxic working environments present to our bodies, minds and souls. It shows what cases of serious burnout can look like: Bartleby becomes completely unable to continue to perform at work. Or, perhaps, he grows unwilling – this point is left open for interpretation. He ceases to accept literal and metaphorical nourishment; he becomes ever more immobile and withdrawn. He can no longer work, but he is also unable to leave the office. He is drawn to brick walls and dead-ends – external symbols of his state of hopelessness. Bartleby has, quite literally, hit a wall and come to a point where there is no possibility of progress or healing without outside help. He constitutes a serious HR problem for his line-manager, who would certainly be in violation of modern occupational health and dignity at work policies, and who fails in his duty to protect his employee. Bartleby, then, is many things simultaneously – a victim, a refusenik and an accusation, but also a spanner in the machine of competitive capitalism, provoking pity and fear in equal measure.

What, then, can we learn from Bartleby? And how

can his example help us not to turn into ghost-workers ourselves? First and foremost, his story is of course a cautionary tale. We should not seek to emulate the forlorn copyist's death-seeking ways, and we should, if we can, stay clear of working environments such as the narrator's windowless offices on Wall Street. Miserably gazing at the obstacles and horrors in our lives and letting ourselves waste away cannot be the right path, either. By contrast, there is tremendous soft power in Bartleby's mantra, 'I would prefer not to'. It's an excellent starting point. What would *you* prefer not to do anymore?

A recent popular self-help trend revolves around the idea of simply saying 'fuck it' to other people who expect us to do certain things. This teenage, and, let's face it, profoundly anti-social stance is sold as a spiritual act: In *F**K It: The Ultimate Spiritual Way* (2007), for example, John C. Parkin writes: 'When you say F**K It, you carry out a spiritual act (the ultimate one, actually) because you give up, let go, stop resisting and relax back into the natural flow of life itself (otherwise known as the Tao, God, etc.).'[7] Parkin advises us to 'say F**k It to the cleaning and get a cleaner instead', just to walk out of jobs we don't like, to eat chocolate all day if we feel like it, and to take plenty of sick days.[8] There is a childish and arrogant disregard here for the impact of our actions on others and for the economic realities in which we are embedded – most of us can't afford just to walk out of our jobs, regardless of how miserable they may make us, because we have bills to pay and kids to feed. The majority of us can't afford cleaners, either. And even if we can, refusing to clean the house just means somebody else has to do it. Finally, just giving in to every short-term pleasure-seeking impulse is also clearly going to have considerable adverse effects both on our health and on our relationships.

Bartleby's 'I would prefer not to' is a more ethical response than simply saying 'fuck it' to the many obligations in which we might find ourselves entangled. Why? It's a gentler, less aggressive statement that articulates our own desires without diminishing those of others. What Bartleby is really saying is: 'I don't want to do this anymore, I can't really do this anymore, for it hurts my soul and it breaks my heart.' He is saying: 'This is making me ill, please don't ask me to do it.' And while he may not get as far as to wonder, 'Is there another way? A compromise?', we should.

What are the things in your life that jar with your deeper values, that are in conflict with your basic needs, that make you depressed or anxious? Who or what has pushed you into that in-between place where the ghost-like dwell, in which you feel neither properly alive nor dead? For burnout is just such a liminal zone. It's a state in which we are suspended between health and illness, life and death, unable either to work or to rest, in which we remain fixated and immobile like Bartleby, and as incapable as he is of experiencing joy. And often we forget completely what used to give us pleasure and energy. Again, like Bartleby, we can only think of what we don't want to do anymore.

In coaching, these kinds of negative, avoidant, moving-away-from aims are called 'dead man's goals'. And that is very apt, for dead people are the true masters of not working, smoking, drinking, overeating or under-exercising, and not worrying or feeling tired anymore. Let us therefore counter Bartleby's repetitive rejoinder with a question: 'What would you prefer to do instead?' We can't heal if we don't have a positive vision of what we want to do with our life when we are whole again. We can't heal if all we can focus on is what we don't want to do anymore. The lack of a positive vision and even just a single affirmative preference was precisely why Bartleby didn't make it in the end. We can learn from his example, but only if we make that further, positive step of imagining what would be good for us, and then seeking to achieve it.

H is for Heaviness

I have always been fascinated by the metaphors we use to describe our inner lives. Often things of beauty, they are also very telling. Metaphors matter, especially our mind metaphors. Those metaphors are attempts to capture our feelings, experiences and sensations by imagining them as something else that is similar in some way. What exactly goes on inside us is often hard to describe in plain language. Metaphors allow us to share what we are thinking and feeling with others. Verbal imagery can also help us to recognise and to make sense of what happens in our inland empires. Mind metaphors illuminate the diffuse and shifting forces of dark and light within us.

But, in turn, the mind metaphors that are dominant in our culture can also shape our individual lived experiences. Think, for example, of the insidious mind-as-computer metaphor. It encourages us to think of our inner life as being determined by hard-wiring, programming, glitches, overload, depleted batteries, on-and-off switches and psychological malware. This metaphorical cluster is less than helpful because we are in no way like computers. And nor should we aspire to be. We are relational and creative – embodied, embedded and encultured, constantly interacting with our environments. Nor are we machines, clockworks or automatons. We get tired and depleted and, if we are not careful, we might even burn out. We need regularly to stop and rest and replenish our energies, and this is also what makes us human.

In descriptions of what their exhaustion feels like, my coaching clients often use imagery that revolves around empty batteries, empty tanks, overdrawn accounts and depletion. They are based on the idea of our life force as a precious and limited resource that we need to manage with great care. The notion of burnout (itself a metaphor) indicates that we have used up a limited quantity of something too quickly because we were burning the candle at both ends. Again, these metaphors are not helpful, for they are fatalistic. When we are burnt out, when our batteries are empty and when we have expended all our energy, we cannot replenish ourselves. We have squandered our limited allowance, and the implication is that it is our own fault.

A much more helpful metaphor for states of exhaustion is the notion of heaviness. Heaviness imagery revolves around the sensation of being weighed down by the burden of our thoughts, bodies, tasks and sorrows. Heaviness metaphors have always chimed with me. When I'm exhausted, all activity, including standing and walking, uses energy I don't have. Walking is an effort, my legs feel as if glued to the ground. To move, I have to wage a battle against invisible strings. Just being alive and human feels like work. My speech becomes slow, my eyes turn to slits, wanting to close. Gravity's laws are torture. It feels like the cosmos has conspired to pull me down.

There is a beautiful German word that fits well with this imagery cluster, *Schwermut* (heavy + courage). We could translate it as the difficulty of conjuring up courage, or else as our spirit being weighed down or depressed by something. *Schwermut* designates a paralysing state of mind that is defined by sadness, hopelessness and an inner emptiness. A profound heaviness of heart and soul. The word 'depression', too, centres on the sensation of an inner heaviness. It comes from the Latin word *deprimere*, 'to press down, depress'.

We can also find links to this sensation of heaviness in the present-day diagnostic criteria of depression, for example in the form of the slowness of thoughts and movements, or 'psychomotor retardation'. The *Diagnostic and Statistical Manual of Mental Disorders 5* lists a 'slowing down of thought and a reduction of physical movement (observable by others, not merely subjective feelings of restlessness or being slowed down)' as one of depression's core symptoms.

The poets and painters of the past, too, have clearly felt the relentless pull of gravity when they were in a state of exhaustion. Remember the description of Belacqua, a character in Dante's *The Divine Comedy* (see 'D is for Dante')? Belacqua, lying in the shade behind a boulder at the foot of a mountain he is too weary to climb, is listless and exhausted: He sits with his arms around his knees, his head bent downwards. Dante describes him as someone 'who shows / Himself more idle, than if laziness / Were sister to him'.[1] Dante notes the heavy slowness of Belacqua's movements, that he is stingy with his words and that he lifts his eyes just high enough to be able to see his visitors.

Albrecht Dürer's famous engraving *Melencolia I* (1514)

depicts the heavy energetic cost of thinking. His picture shows a dejected female figure, who, with her head in her hand, sits surrounded by the scattered paraphernalia of science and art. She stares gloomily into the distance. Listlessly, she holds a geometrical tool in her lap but is too weary to use it. An hourglass in the background signals that she is wasting time and that it is running out. A set of empty scales indicates that she may have lost her sense of balance; a scattering of tools suggests that she has probably worked too hard, and on too many different projects simultaneously. An emaciated sleeping dog and a limp, depressed-looking putto with a bowed head further reinforce the all-pervasive sense of exhaustion. Although the tools of critical reasoning are within touching distance, the woman is simply too weary to act, literally and metaphorically weighed down by the boundless possibilities. Her head has become too heavy for her to hold upright. Her thoughts and her very capacity to think and reason have become an intolerable burden.

In the film *Melancholia* (2011), the Danish director Lars von Trier provides another striking image of the tremendous effort it takes to drag our bodies across the earth when we are exhausted. The film's main character, the melancholic Justine, sinks into a state of clinical depression after her wedding night. She is so exhausted that she cannot wash herself, and is barely able to leave her room. She describes her condition to her sister as akin to wading through a field of grey yarn, which is slowing her movements and pulling her to the ground. She drags herself around the house like a zombie. She can barely muster the energy to keep her eyes open; they are always half-closed, the lids, too, being pulled downwards.

Why are heaviness and the tyranny of gravity such powerful images of what exhaustion feels like? In *Metaphors We Live By* (1980), the linguists George Lakoff and Mark Johnson offer a possible answer. They argue that our metaphors are often rooted in embodied experiences and perceptions. There might, then, be a rather literal explanation for heaviness metaphors: exhaustion and sadness impact our bodies. When we are depleted or dejected, we quite literally have no energy to hold ourselves upright. Instead, we bow our heads, curve our backs, and allow our shoulders to slump forward. We walk, sit and stand as though we are carrying a sack full of stones on our back. And there is of course the idea of our thoughts becoming oppressive despots – dark forces that put pressure on our spirit and life force, urging us towards inactivity and collapse.

But here is the main reason why I like heaviness imagery: it is because heaviness can be a temporary state, rather than a permanent condition. Unlike being burnt out, or permanently depleted, like an empty battery or a drained reservoir, feeling heavy can be overcome. The clouds of heaviness can lift. And when they do, we once again feel light. We have a spring in our step, like young deer bounding gracefully across a clearing. We become bird-like, sailing the wind, seemingly without effort. Our bodies are no longer burdens. Our thoughts levitate. Our entire being aspires towards the sky. We are once again amongst the effortlessly upright, our necks tall, proud spires, and gravity can go hang.

I is for Inner Critic

Most of us will be familiar with a negative voice in our head that constantly criticises and judges us. It's the voice that tells us we are not clever enough, not likeable enough, that we are too fat, too thin, too short, too tall, that the book we have written is no good, that the dress we have bought is ill-fitting, that the present we gave to a friend wasn't right, that the meal we cooked for that dinner party was a disaster, that we are catastrophic at our job, that we don't know how to maintain good friendships. This voice has many names: inner critic, judge, saboteur, demon, gremlin, chimp, superego. Choose your metaphor.

In psychological frameworks, the inner critic's activities are described as automatic negative thoughts or as negative self-talk. This inner critic is never satisfied and can soil and spoil anything we may achieve – no matter how impressive. It magnifies the negative and spreads discontent, and worse, in our lives. It can be a cruel and deeply damaging force. Its strength and impact determine our overall mental well-being. It can drain our energy from within and be the major internal cause of our exhaustion. When we suffer from an overactive inner critic, we expend most of our energy in endless psychological warfare with ourselves. Consequently, we have much less energy available to direct outwards, into our projects and into building relationships with the people for whom we care and who care for us.

If our inner critic were a person, we would avoid them like the plague. They would fall into the category of the bully or even the outright abuser: someone who systematically erodes our sense of self-worth, who mocks, berates, belittles and demeans us, and who constantly accuses us of appalling crimes. Our inner critic tends to make us feel ashamed, guilty, small and miserable. We would never tolerate this kind of talk from somebody else. If it were directed at a child, a friend or someone we love, we would intervene. Why, then, do so many of us accept it as our own grim normality?

The Buddhist psychologist Tara Brach argues that most of us are trapped in what she calls a 'trance of unworthiness'. Many people think that there is something wrong with them, and they see the world through a lens of personal insufficiency.[1] My experience as a coach certainly testifies to the truth of that insight. It is heart-breaking to see how many of my clients have a completely unjustifiable but firmly held negative opinion of themselves. Regardless of how successful they are, and how impressive their lives may look from the outside, many of them struggle with profoundly negative beliefs about themselves. High-powered CEOs, founders of hugely successful businesses and internationally respected academics believe themselves to be clueless imposters, and live in dread of being publicly unmasked as incompetent frauds. Talented artists and writers think their work is worthless, and believe that the people who buy, exhibit, publish or simply love it have made grievous errors of judgement. Caring and committed mothers and fathers think they are catastrophic parents who are ruining their children's mental health, inflicting one trauma after another. Highly intelligent women think they are profoundly stupid; much-loved and inspirational team leaders think they are criminally incompetent. What is going on?

Most psychologists agree that those critical voices are rooted in our childhoods. The founding father of psychoanalysis, Sigmund Freud, famously divided the psychological apparatus into three entities: the id, the ego and the superego. The id is made up of our raw drives and urges, our fantasies and dark desires. The ego is the part of our minds that is committed to the reality principle. It finds itself in the tricky position of having to negotiate between the instinctual desires of the id and the judgements of the superego. The superego is the critical and moralising part of our minds, and it maps quite neatly onto the idea of the inner critic. Freud argued that our superegos are formed by internalising external views of ourselves – predominantly those of our parents.[2] If our parents were highly critical of us or excessively demanding, it is likely that our superegos will reflect that.

But our superego also internalises wider social expectations and cultural norms, and starts to generate what Freud calls 'ego ideals' – a unique concoction of moral standards for ourselves, of which we then tend regularly to fall short. Ego ideals manifest in the many 'shoulds', 'musts' and 'coulds' that populate our minds. Freud's superego can be a cruel and self-flagellating force, which sadistically punishes and tyrannises the ego. If our super-ego is in overdrive, we spend most of our psychological energy on inner battles and have little to give to the outside world. Franz Kafka was one of the greatest explorers of that experience. In his celebrated story *The Metamorphosis* (1915) he showed how thinking of oneself as no better than a verminous bug can turn you into one. Many of the characters in his fiction are locked into exhausting and often fatal struggles with an inner critic, which he traced back to his own father. Like those characters in Kafka's fiction, we may deem ourselves unworthy and despicable, and expect the world to see us in that way, too. Because this is an unpleasant and energy-draining state to be in, we may also be more prone to poor coping strategies in an attempt to numb this relentless torturer in our heads. For more than two decades, I tried to drown mine in red wine (unsuccessfully, of course).

A more scientific explanation of the origins of our inner critic locates it in particular parts of our brains. More specifically, psychologists have argued that we have a primitive 'survivor brain' that encompasses the brain stem, the older part of our brain that is tasked with physical survival and the fight-or-flight response to danger. This part of our brain is highly attuned to potential threats. Hyper-vigilant, it is constantly on the lookout for danger. It also involves the limbic system and the amygdala, which regulate our emotional responses and can trigger the emission of the stress hormone cortisol.[3]

By tracing it back to this primal function, one can see that our inner critic originally had a positive function:

to ensure our survival. This not only includes spotting threats (like sabre-toothed tigers), but also telling us specific stories about ourselves and others that are bearable. Children who feel unloved, or who are constantly criticised or are the victims of abuse, for example, will tend to blame themselves rather than their parents. This may seem counterintuitive, but it isn't. Young children depend completely on their parents' care for survival. The conscious acknowledgement of our parents' unfairness, cruelty, incompetency or inability to love us is an insight so distressing that many can only face it in adulthood, after years of therapy, and even then it is difficult to bear. It is much safer for a child to turn their criticism inward and to blame themselves for the misfortunes they are suffering. However, what might have been a sad but sensible survival mechanism in childhood can turn into a truly debilitating handicap in adulthood.

In Cognitive Behavioural Therapy (CBT), the inner critic is reduced to its output: automatic negative thoughts. Automatic negative thoughts, CBT therapists believe, are driven by our core beliefs. We can think of our automatic negative thoughts as the situational expressions of our most negative beliefs about ourselves.[4] Common core beliefs that are harmful usually come in the form of rigid 'I am …', 'People are …', and 'The world is …' statements. We may, for example, think that we are unlovable, incompetent, ugly, stupid or existentially flawed in some other way. Our inner critic will then constantly broadcast messages that can be traced back to these problematic assumptions. It may say things such as: 'You are a big, fat loser, and you will never achieve anything in your life.' It may say: 'Nobody likes you. You don't have any friends.' It may constantly draw attention to our perceived faults and shortcomings. It may belittle our achievements, dismissing them as luck or accidents. It may relentlessly badger us for past mistakes or paralyse us with disparaging remarks in the present.

Our inner critic also has the power to make us feel anxious and fearful. Hyper-vigilant, it may incessantly point out danger, both to our physical and psychological health. It may catastrophise, exaggerate and magnify the bad and minimise the good in our lives. It may engage in paranoid mind-reading, attributing bad motives to other people's words and actions. It may live in constant expectation of punishment and falling from grace, and fixate on signs of lost love in our interactions with others. Hyper-sensitively attuned to danger signals and with a relentless focus on what could go wrong, it may instil in us chronic anxiety.

There is, however, a great paradox at the heart of the inner critic. For one of its core functions is to stop us from feeling what we don't want to feel, because, crucially, the inner critic is a creature of thought. When our inner critic is active, we are caught up in thoughts – negative thoughts, for sure, but nevertheless thoughts rather than feelings. When my inner critic is active I don't feel anything. I lose touch with my sadness, anger or fear. Of course these thoughts make us feel bad, too, but they make us feel bad in a specific way. Above all, they trigger self-contempt and self-loathing. What our inner critic prevents us from feeling is usually sadness. Indeed, one of its core functions is to keep our sadness at bay. Sadness is an emotion, whereas self-contempt and self-loathing are mental states that rest on (usually baseless) cognitive judgements produced by our minds. And when our inner critic is switched on, we stay in that analytical thinking zone – unpleasant as it may be. But it is, as they say, the devil we know.

How, then, can we lessen the impact of our inner critic and liberate all the energy that is expended by our struggle with it? To challenge our inner critic CBT-style, we must seek to oppose what it tells us rationally by confronting it with objective facts.[5] This entails taking seriously what the inner critic tells us and trying to convince it logically that it is wrong. This method resembles a journalistic fact-checking exercise, designed to counter and discredit fake news in our inner realm. However, this constant rational countering of what our mind dishes up can become exhausting in its own right. Acceptance and Commitment Therapy (ACT) offers a different and more helpful approach. It focuses not on changing our negative cognitions and beliefs, but on how we can accept them and then try to let them go.[6] The ACT way of disempowering our inner critic accepts that we have far less control over our thoughts and feelings than we like to think.

In my work as a coach, I have found that the ACT-based approach is the most effective. It entails getting to know our inner critic, naming it, observing what it does without judgement and then letting it go. The first step is to understand what exactly our inner critic is telling us, what triggers it, and also where it might be coming from. An understanding of its core message, patterns and origins can help us to treat ourselves more compassionately. We will then begin to realise that these thoughts are neither true nor our fault, and we will be able to put a healing distance between ourselves and our inner critic.

The ACT practitioner Russ Harris treats the voice of the inner critic as mind-chatter and seeks to shift attention away from the content (what it has to say) to the form (insignificant noise in our head).[7] Most importantly, Harris suggests that we simply observe our inner critic when it is speaking, without 'fusing' with what it has to say. In that way, we will learn to separate the voice of the inner critic from our true essence. ACT teaches us that we are not our negative thoughts. We can learn to 'de-fuse' from them by turning them into objects of our critical discernment rather than accepting them as the truth about ourselves and others.

When we observe our inner critic in action, we may want to remind ourselves that our thoughts are just words and that our beliefs are just that: beliefs, not facts. They are nothing more than the unhelpful noise of our endlessly chattering minds. There is a massive difference between thinking that we are unlovable and don't have any friends, and thinking that our inner critic is telling us that we are unlovable and don't have any friends. When our inner critic bombards us with unhelpful thoughts, we can resolve not to take the content of these thoughts too seriously. We may say: 'There's the inner critic again, doing its dirty work.' Just adding, 'I think that …' or 'I notice I think that …' before our negative thoughts can dramatically lessen their effect.

Harris compares our minds to the mini-conveyor belts that rotate dishes past diners' tables in a sushi bar. Those

73

belts present a continuous succession of different options that travel past us. Some of these dishes look appetising and we may choose to put them on our table and eat them. Others don't, and we simply let them pass. We can practise doing the same with unhelpful thoughts. We do not have to engage with every thought our mind presents to us, and we do not need to let them spoil our meal.

Another potent ACT metaphor is that of passengers on a bus. Harris invites us to imagine our mind as resembling a bus: we are in the driving seat, but there are also numerous passengers in the back of the vehicle. They are there to stay, and we can't ever get rid of them. They are simply the fellow travel companions that fate has dealt us. Some of these passengers are nice and kind, some are difficult and challenging, some are quiet and some are loud. All of them try to influence where we are going. Some have wise things to say, others do not. One of those is our inner critic. He is the most vocal and rowdy passenger on the bus, often shouting abuse from the back. He tries to persuade us not to go where we truly want to go, instead trying to make us stop, turn back, or head off down dangerous roads. While we would of course love to kick this particular passenger off our bus for good, we have to accept that we can't. Instead, we must learn not to listen to him. We can listen instead to the smarter and kinder passengers. They tend to be quieter and more difficult to hear, but they are there and have important insights to share. We can train ourselves to perceive what that critical passenger has to say as meaningless noise. Most importantly, we should never ever let him become the backseat driver.

J is for Joy

When our lives feel flat and our spirits languish, we can fall prey to anhedonia – the inability to experience pleasure in life. With our senses dulled and emotions numbed, everything can appear to be drained of colour, as though someone has activated a cosmic greyscale filter. When we are in the grip of anhedonia, we often cannot even remember what used to bring us joy, and what it feels like to be properly alive, engaged, connected and full of zest. If that is you, then I urge you to find a hobby. This is not facetious advice for the following reasons: hobbies serve no purpose other than making the person who performs them happy. Like child's play, they are unapologetically non-instrumental activities. They cannot be monetised nor utilised. The word hobby derives from *hobi*, a 'small, active horse', and is a shortening of 'hobbyhorse' – a child's toy, typically a wooden stick with a cloth-made horse's head on it. Hobby has come to signify a favourite pursuit, object or topic, but also, more importantly, an 'activity that doesn't go anywhere'. And it is precisely because they 'don't go anywhere' that hobbies can lead us out of the barren flatlands of our exhaustion.

It is actually quite difficult, if not impossible, to find a hobby that genuinely serves no other function than to give us pleasure. A hobby in the strict sense is not about learning new skills, gaining cultural capital, or engaging in photogenic status-enhancing activities that we can later share on Instagram. Hobbies should not even serve the primary purpose of improving our health and reducing our stress levels (although plenty of research suggests they do).[1] And nor should a hobby become just another arena in which we wrestle with our perfectionism, or seek to excel. Hobbies must not generate any other value than pleasure. Hobbies, by their very nature, challenge utilitarian beliefs. They are atelic activities – activities without *telos*, an ultimate aim.

Hobbies also violate our competitive performance ethos. People who have hobbies and whose hobbies make them happy tend to be those who have 'given themselves the broadest permission for failure and imperfection. They revel in the process of making a table rather than feel pressure to sell it once it is finished.'[2] In other words, hobbies should also be achievement- and competition-free zones. This is a question not so much of the specific activities we choose as our hobbies, but of our disposition while we are engaging in them – our attitude to what we do. It doesn't matter whether we are good at our hobby or not. In fact, we can completely suck at our hobby and that's absolutely fine.

My father, for example, has been playing the trombone since he was twelve. It was the only instrument left that his school could lend to those wanting to learn music but who couldn't afford to buy one. Nobody had picked the battered brass trombone, so my father did. And he has remained fiercely loyal to it ever since. He practised religiously every day. Decades later, he bought himself the finest trombone he could find. He hired a teacher, he plays in a jazz band. And yet he would be the first to admit that he is not particularly gifted at playing the trombone, and never really was. The trombone is not only a loud but also an unforgiving wind instrument. Its long cylindrical metal tube with two turns and a bell, its movable slides, complicated valve system and cup-shaped mouthpiece, which requires trembling lips to create a decent sound, are incredibly difficult to master for those of average musical ability. It is fair to say that my father, even after sixty years of patient practice, has not yet succeeded in fully mastering his instrument. And yet that simply doesn't matter. He loves playing it, and that's all that counts.

The reason why taking up a hobby nowadays is akin to a radical act is because the non-value-generating nature of hobbies runs completely counter to our basic cultural conditioning. As the time-management expert Oliver Burkeman writes: 'In an age of instrumentalization, the hobbyist is a subversive: he insists that some things are worth doing for themselves alone, despite offering no pay-offs in terms of productivity or profit.'³ We have completely internalised the injunction never to waste time, to aim to excel at everything we do and to squeeze learning or personal advantage out of all our activities – including our leisure pursuits. If we can't optimise our health or up our coolness factor, why bother doing something? The simple and revolutionary answer is because it brings us joy. And sadly, the art of cultivating joy – essential for dragging ourselves out of the wastelands of exhaustion – is something many of us have become increasingly unable to do.

Hobbies also differ from self-care. Self-care, as we have come to understand it in the West, thanks to the efforts of the marketing multitudes, is purpose-driven. Its function is to restore our energies so that we can continue to be productive in our value-generating jobs, or to go on performing smoothly as mothers, partners or carers. Self-care therefore isn't really a form of caring at all, at least not in a caring for caring's sake kind of way. The notion of self-care is just another way of urging us to manage our energies more productively, to schedule 'me-time' to recharge so that we don't burn out. Self-care, then, is not about joy or pleasure, but rather about boosting the human instrument. The German philosopher Friedrich Nietzsche was already aware of this dilemma. In *The Gay Science* (1882), he anticipated the twisted logic of Western self-care.

> How frugal our educated people ... have become regarding 'joy'! How they are becoming increasingly suspicious of all joy! More and more, work enlists all good conscience on its side; the desire for joy already calls itself a 'need to recuperate' and is becoming ashamed of itself. 'One owes it to one's health' – that is what people say when they are caught on an excursion into the country. Soon we may well reach the point where people can no longer give in to the desire for a *vita contemplativa* (that is, taking a walk with ideas and friends) without self-contempt and a bad conscience.[4]

Hobbies are different. They are radically purposeless, immune to being co-opted in our quest for optimising ourselves or recharging our dwindling energy resources. True hobbyists embrace futility, indulging in the wonderfully pointless: they construct ships in bottles or model aeroplanes that can't fly. They spend hours in basements painting little tin soldiers or building elaborately looping model train layouts. They quilt, sew, or knit stuff that could never be worn by anyone or sold on Etsy. They may be birdwatchers or trainspotters, grow rare succulents or crooked bonsai trees, or accumulate thousands of miniature angel figurines. They may collect first editions of seventeenth-century cookbooks, postcards of hot Victorian men with moustaches, rare art nouveau dining sets, or small white stones with holes in them. Whatever works, as long as it isn't put to work.

I have three hobbies. I run, about three or four times a week. I run in the early mornings, just after the sun has risen. I run along the river that meanders through Canterbury, or in the nearby woods, across fields and meadows, or up the steep hill from where our university looks down on the city. I run without ever measuring the distance I cover, or my speed. I'm not training for anything – not a 5k, not a 10k, not a marathon. On good days, when I feel like it, I run long and fast and hard; on sluggish days, I choose shorter routes and am overtaken by old ladies on rusty bikes. I don't wish to lose weight or to become super-fit. I've settled for what is on both counts. I run simply because it makes me happy. I love being in nature when it wakes up; I get pleasure from feeling my strength and speed. I listen to music that makes my heart sing, and sometimes to the birds and the rustling of the wind in the willows and the murmurings of the waters of the Stour. I like to see how the seasons change, how the grass grows green and tall and then turns yellow and dies. I've watched seven cygnets grow from fluff-grey, clumsy creatures into proud white swans soaring around in a V-shape. My favourite time is autumn because I'm a melancholic and I see beauty in decline. I like the smell of rotting leaves.

I also play the piano, strictly only Baroque music, and never anything written after 1750, jolly or atonal. I play only for myself. I'm about as musical as my father is. But some musical phrases make my soul sing, and I play them over and over again and feel deeply moved. Perhaps my least suitable but by far most cherished hobby is Thai kickboxing. It's roughly in the same category as basketball for me, which I played with great passion as a teenager – but then, wisely, was convinced to give up (I am 5 feet 3 inches tall). I am happy to admit that I have zero talent when it comes to boxing, kicking, wrestling and jumping. I couldn't hop onto a chair if the floor were lava, and my hand-to-foot coordination has always been geriatric. I am doing OK at long-distance running simply because it requires perseverance and I am extremely tenacious. I'm a complete outlier in the world of Muay Thai – I will never become a fighter or a stuntwoman, nor would I last longer than thirty seconds in a confrontation with a real-life thug. I haven't even reached friendly sparring level yet.

I know all this, and I'm probably a sorry sight in my oversized gloves and shin guards, my movements always a heartbeat or three too slow to be effective. My performance is a far cry from the gracefully whirling and swirling martial artists in Wong Kar Wai's *The Grandmaster*, who always look like they are dancing or mating rather than fighting. And yet, I find my twice-weekly Muay Thai practice deeply, even existentially satisfying. I'd never miss it for anything. I have an amazingly wise and patient trainer, who probably sees me as his greatest professional challenge yet – or as some kind of Karmic visitation, bestowed upon him for past life sins. We were both tremendously relieved and rather surprised when I passed my first Khan exam. After fifty private lessons, that is. I plan to continue my training into old age, and to remain as loyal to this sport as my father is to his trombone.

Hobbies, then, especially the ill-fitting, futile and strange, can bring joy back into our lives. But joy also lies elsewhere, in the most unforeseen places and moments and encounters – sights of random beauty, meetings with magnificent creatures, unexpected acts of kindness, spontaneous expressions of love and care. Our uncaged spirit knows where to find it, amongst the garbage and the flowers, in poems and in songs. Perhaps we will encounter it contemplating a red wheelbarrow, glazed with rain water, beside the white chickens. We may find it when a stranger helps us to collect the lemons that have spilled from our grocery bag, in men and women who walk in beauty, like the night, in the thing with feathers that perches in our souls, in the presence of still waters, where the great herons feed. We may find it in our cat's effortlessly elegant jump onto the breakfast table, our child's smudged drawing of a dancing wolf, in our lover's eyes when they laugh at our jokes. Joy may hide in the stone, the dirt, the dust as much as it does in lust.

K is for Kaizen

Any kind of sustainable change requires perseverance, because the fantasy of instantaneous magical transformation is just that – a fantasy. This also holds true for our exhaustion. Dragging ourselves out of a state of exhaustion demands persistent effort, a steady determination to reconnect with what we value and what truly matters to us, as well as learning to let go of and to say no to what doesn't. A question I ask all those I coach is: What don't you have to do anymore? This can include tasks we should learn to delegate to others, but can also touch on more existential matters. To which demands on our time and attention should we say no – in both our private and our working lives? Do we still need to try and please certain people? What would happen if we stopped trying to earn our friends' approval by chasing status? Do we really still need to live according to our parents' playbook?

On our journey from exhaustion to vitality, we will often take steps in the right direction, only to find ourselves being pulled back again. But if we persist, we will eventually see gradual improvement. And gradual improvement is in fact all that we can ever achieve. Sudden transformations never work. The Japanese concept of *kaizen* can help us to appreciate that the art of self-improvement is a lifelong process. It translates as 'good improvement', or 'change for the better', and encapsulates a philosophy of continuous and incremental improvement.[1]

Although rooted in ancient ideas, kaizen rose to prominence in Japan after the Second World War, in the context of what became known as the 'Toyota Way'. The Toyota car manufacturer put into practice a simple but radical method. It deemed no improvement too small, regardless of how trivial it might seem. Whenever anyone noted an error or a suboptimal process in the production line, everything was halted, and the entire team would come together to analyse it. No less importantly, all improvements were implemented immediately.

While Frederick Winslow Taylor and Henry Ford also sought to improve their production processes, they did not involve their workers in developing better practices, but dictated scientifically derived efficiency-enhancement measures from above. Toyota's approach, by contrast, was bottom-up, drawing on the collective experience of the workforce. Workers were empowered to co-create the success of the brand. They felt that their ideas and expertise mattered, and that their views were valued. Toyota thus managed to create a participatory culture of continuous and systematic improvement, which, over time, resulted not just in high worker engagement and job satisfaction but also significant gains in efficiency and productivity.

This approach seems to emerge naturally from more deeply-held Japanese cultural beliefs, as is evident in the Japanese proverb: 'With many little strokes a large tree is felled.' However, this small-step, collaborative work improvement approach had first been used in the US, in

the Training Within Industry (TWI) programme implemented during the Second World War. Owing to a serious
lack of resources and time, the TWI method suggested
that producers of urgently needed war equipment focus on
manageable small-scale improvements that could be implemented immediately. There was simply no time to aim for
bigger strategic changes. Instead, the goal was to make
the best use of what was already there, and to encourage
workers to suggest improvements. After the war, as part
of the Marshall Plan, American experts were charged
with helping to rebuild Japan's industry. In the 1950s,
American delegates introduced the TWI programmes to
Japanese managers, and kaizen principles, filtered through
a Western business lens, were thus re-introduced to their
land of origin. When the Japanese car industry became
highly successful and a serious competitor to the US in the
1980s, Americans, in turn, wanted to understand what was
going on in Japan. Masaaki Imai, a Japanese business con-
sultant, enlightened them in his bestselling book, *Kaizen:
The Key to Japan's Competitive Success* (1986).[2]

Although it rose to prominence in the industrial world,
the principles of kaizen have since migrated into various
other domains, including psychology, healthcare and
coaching. A measured and continuous approach to sustainable habit change, kaizen is now considered a general
philosophy of improvement that focuses on small steps,
details and marginal gains. Humans are, of course, nothing
like production processes. We are also not management
problems to be solved, and I am not a fan of the language
of optimisation and maximisation. But there is much to

be said for kaizen's emphasis on meticulous, daily reform rather than flamboyant, radical revolution. It is a refreshingly down-to-earth model in the self-help landscape, where many thrive on selling quick-fix solutions. Kaizen highlights the fact that little that is worthwhile can ever be achieved without hard work, and that we have to earn our successes. Moreover, kaizen is related to two important ancient virtues: patience and perseverance.

Perseverance features high on the psychologist Angela Duckworth's list of key prerequisites for success in life.[3] In her bestseller *Grit: Why Passion and Resilience are the Secrets to Success* (2017), she argues that although natural talent matters, perseverance always tops aptitude as a predictor of achievement. Duckworth's findings tally nicely with the moral of Aesop's famous fable, 'The Tortoise and the Hare'. Although the hare is obviously far more gifted at running than the tortoise, it is the tenacious reptilian who ends up winning the race. The naturally talented hare is arrogant and lazy, overestimates his own abilities and underestimates those of his opponent. He showily dashes off and takes the lead, but, too sure of his victory, decides to take a nap half-way. The tortoise crosses the finishing line just as the hare wakes up again. Duckworth understands grit as a drive to improve our skills and performance by consistent effort. Gritty people are dogged, always eager to learn and never satisfied or complacent.

Importantly, grit also requires the ability to learn from our failures. Learning from what hasn't worked well, or could work better in the future, is also essential in the kaizen process. Rather than being embarrassed or discouraged by it, gritty people see failure as a learning opportunity. They tend to have what the psychologist Carol S. Dweck calls a 'growth mindset'.[4] Dweck argues that the hallmark of such a mindset is a 'passion for stretching yourself and sticking to it, even (or especially) when it's not going well'.[5] People with a growth mindset firmly believe in the possibility of developing their abilities.

Like the Toyota workers, those with a growth mindset are genuinely interested in trying to understand where they went wrong. Kaizen, however, is not just about cherishing incremental improvement, perseverance, cultivating growth mindsets and establishing progressive failure-processing cultures. It is also about doing the next right thing. During those dark nights of the soul, when all hope is gone and we feel lost and alone, we still have one option: to do the next right thing. When Anna in the Disney film *Frozen II* (2019) believes that two of the people she loved most on earth, her sister Elsa and her best friend Olaf, are dead, she finds herself both literally and metaphorically at the bottom of a deep, dark cave. She just lies there, crying and cradling herself in a foetal position. Her grief is so intense that she can't muster the strength to get up.

But then a voice emerges, calmly and insistently telling her to do the next right thing. Eventually she gets up and begins the long and arduous climb from the bottom of the cave towards the light. She never looks far ahead, just breaking it down to the next step. And so she clambers through the night, stumbling blindly towards the light. She climbs higher and higher, and eventually reaches the mouth of the cave and steps into the daylight. This scene resonates nicely with Confucius' saying: 'The man who moves a mountain begins by carrying away small stones.'

We all have what the psychologist Robert Kegan calls an inbuilt 'immunity to change'. When we ask too much of ourselves, when we aim for a transformation that is too radical and threatening, or when we seek to implement drastic habit changes too suddenly, our fight or flight response might kick in. Most of us are naturally change-averse, our minds focused on what we may lose rather than on what we have to gain. We may procrastinate, or simply set ourselves up for failure. We may never be able to let go of the secondary gain we derive from unproductive behaviours, and may hold on to our bad habits simply because they are the devil we know. Kaizen-style change, however, tricks the system that wishes to keep things as they are. It is so gradual, and often so easy, that we tend not to be too alarmed by the prospect of embarking on it. So, instead of seeking to eliminate all our stressors at work and at home at once, we may start with choosing just one, and take one small step at a time to tackle it. If we want to change our working patterns, we can commence by identifying one small habit that is not serving us and concentrate our efforts on that. And if we wish to seek more balance in our lives, we can begin by going for a very short walk each day, or try to meet a friend in a café or for a drink at least once a week.

Crucially, kaizen puts the emphasis on the process rather than the outcome. It encourages us to see ourselves as lifelong learners, seekers of growth and knowledge who will never be done with the task of improving ourselves. As

the philosopher Jonathan Rowson writes: 'We are unfin-
ished business. There is always scope to grow, not just
intellectually but morally, epistemically and spiritually.'[6]
We can begin by asking ourselves what small adjustments
we might make in our own lives to improve them right now.
What is our next right thing?

L is for Life-Cost

In the mid-nineteenth century, the American philosopher Henry David Thoreau famously withdrew to a cabin on the banks of Walden Pond in Concord, Massachusetts. It was there that he tried to live simply, supported by the labour of his own hands. He stayed in the woods for over two years. He claimed that he wished to live in a way that was reliant only on the 'necessary of life'.[1] Thoreau's list of essential needs was short and sharp, including only food, shelter, clothing and warmth. By contrast, he felt that most of the 'luxuries' and many of the so-called 'comforts of life', were 'not only dispensable, but positive hindrances to the elevation of mankind'.[2] His aim was to live a life of simplicity and independence.

Above all, Thoreau wished to avoid living a life of what he described as 'quiet desperation'. This, he felt, was the fate of most people.[3] 'Simplify, simplify' was his central motto. He valued his freedom over luxurious carpets and fine furniture, and above haute couture and haute cuisine.[4] 'I went to the woods because I wished to live deliberately, to front only the essential facts of life', he famously wrote,

> and see if I could not learn what it had to teach, and not, when I came to die, discover that I had not lived. … I wanted to live deep and suck out all the marrow

89

of life, to live so sturdily and Spartan-like as to put to rout all that was not life, to cut a broad swath and shave close, to drive life into a corner, and reduce it to its lowest terms.[5]

These were not just catchy minimalist slogans. Thoreau took the economics of simple living seriously. In the first chapter of his bestselling book *Walden* (1854), he introduces the captivating notion of 'life-cost'. Life-cost is a concept that is very different from the cost of living. As Thoreau explains, it is 'the amount of what I will call life which is required to be exchanged for it, immediately or in the long run'.[6] Many of us unthinkingly seek to acquire as much money as possible, and to accumulate as many possessions as our salaries allow. Or else we chase status in the form of degrees, awards, promotion or fame. To obtain as much money or status as we can, we also tend to work as much as we possibly can. In other words, we willingly pay for these things with our time.

Thoreau looked at the question of work from a radically pragmatic perspective. In fact, he turned it upside down. First, he determined his basic needs, without which survival would not be possible. This included how much food and firewood he needed each year, and other non-negotiable essentials. Next, he calculated the exact amount of money he needed to pay for these. His aim was not to work a single hour more than was necessary to cover his basic living expenses. He established that he needed to work only six weeks of the year to cover his minimum expenses. He also chose to earn his money as a day labourer, because it allowed him the freedom to be flexible with his hours. Moreover, he was able to detach completely from his work as soon as it was over.

For the remainder of the year, Thoreau was free to do what he really valued: philosophising and spending time in nature. Material goods, status and social esteem simply had no purchase in his personal value system. Most importantly, his simple, non-materialistic lifestyle allowed him to be the sole master of his own time. He refused to exchange his time for things that ultimately didn't matter to him. For Thoreau, time was both the ultimate currency and the most precious commodity, and he was extremely exacting about how he spent it – every minute mattered. While most of us dedicate much of our waking time to work, he only gave work the absolute bare minimum. Anything more than that would have felt like an existentially bad exchange. We can say, then, that Thoreau anticipated the modern debate about work–life balance, and that he radically privileged the latter. He viewed paid work as a necessary evil to which we should dedicate as little time as possible.

There are many modern-day Thoreaus out there, people who reject materialist rewards in favour of activities that bring them more happiness than commodities ever could. Some reject high-consumption lifestyles for ethical reasons, because they degrade the planet. The members of The Simplicity Collective, for example, voluntarily choose lower incomes and a much lower level of consumption to have more time and energy for finding meaning and satisfaction elsewhere.[7] Very much in Thoreau's spirit, the American social activist Duane Elgin defines voluntary simplicity as 'a way of life that is outwardly simple and inwardly rich ... a deliberate choice to live with less in the belief that more life will be returned to us in the process'.[8] Voluntary simplicity adherents privilege creativity and contemplation over conspicuous consumption. They seek to dedicate the lion's share of their time to 'community or social engagements, more time with family, artistic or intellectual projects, more fulfilling employment, political participation, sustainable living, spiritual exploration, reading, contemplation, relaxation, pleasure-seeking, love, and so on'.[9]

Although voluntary simplicity is still a fairly niche alternative lifestyle concept, numerous psychological studies show that such an approach is more likely to make us happy than the materialist lifestyles that the majority of us lead by default. The psycho-sociologist Tim Kasser, for example, has explored in detail what materialism does to our psyches. The most ardent consumers, he found, tend to be those who are least satisfied with their lives. Avarice and acquisitiveness are not royal roads to happiness, for meaning matters more than money, and relationships always trump consumption. While materialists tend to overvalue objects and status, they undervalue friendships, the quality of their experiences and altruism. They feel fewer positive emotions and are more anxious and depressed than their non-materialist peers. Materialism, Kasser concludes, is in fact seriously detrimental to our psychological well-being.[10]

Also of relevance in this context is the Financial Independence, Retire Early (FIRE) movement. FIRE philosophy promotes aggressive saving, ideally 70 per cent of our income. These savings must be combined with radically decreased expenditure and invested in long-term assets, so that these eventually permit us to live independently. The FIRE money-saving tactics can be truly hard-core, ranging from walking everywhere, renting out our own bedrooms and sleeping on sofas, to living on yellow-sticker super-market items only. The ultimate aim is to retire as early as possible – ideally decades before the standard retire-ment age. While Thoreau asked us to reflect on 'life-cost', FIRE promoters ask us to reflect on how much of our 'life time' we spend at work, and whether what we get out of it in return is worth the expenditure. Do we gain sufficient happiness for our investment of all this time in work? Are our salaries worth the many sacrifices they require? Do we really want to work until we're sixty-five, or is there another way?

Their project, however, differs from Thoreau's and the voluntary simplicity movements' approach in one key respect. It concerns the temporal outlook. FIRE is all about making and saving more money in significantly less time, so that we can spend more time on doing the things we love to do sooner. The FIRE version of simple living is radically future-oriented: the hope is that extreme frugality in the present will result in freedom from work in the future. Sim-plicity or downshifting is not the aim as such, but rather a means to an end. The true goal is gaining as much future free time as possible, as fast as possible. While Thoreau based his 'life-cost' calculations on a single calendar year, FIRE adherents take our entire lifespan into consideration.

Thoreau's carefully calculated privileging of time over wealth, the voluntary simplicity adherents' valuing of inner experiences over consumption, and the FIRE movement followers' favouring of future freedoms over enjoying basic comforts in the present moment may all seem too radical to most of us. These models challenge deeply-held cultural values. They constitute extreme departures from socially sanctioned scripts, demanding a very visible break with what are considered normal ways to live our lives. Yet while we may not feel called to sell up and move into a cabin in the woods, to cancel all conspicuous consumption or to save 70 per cent of our income, we may wish to ask ourselves the following: What is the actual life-cost of our choices? And are the outcomes truly worth the investment?

We may, for example, contemplate taking a new job with a higher salary and more status, but which would require us to spend more time commuting and working longer hours. It would result in our being less able to spend time with family and friends, and would likely also increase our stress and anxiety levels. Would the additional income make up for what we would lose? What exactly would it buy us, and are those purchases genuinely more important than seeing more of our partners, our children and our friends?

Today, the cost of living is so high that there is little scope for life-cost calculations of the kind Thoreau conducted. Most of us will not be in a position that allows us to blow our money on frivolous luxury items. For the vast majority, economic realities and non-negotiable commitments to those for whom we care radically limit our choices. Thoreau, it is worth remembering, was white, male and single, and from a well-off family. He also had a network of friends and family who supported him. He didn't have to pay much for his cabin, and nor did he have to fret over the costs of childcare or gas and electricity. And yet, wherever there is scope to make choices – however small they may be – it is worth remembering that everything comes at a cost. And the currency with which we pay is life time – time that we could spend in other ways, on the things that truly matter to us.

M is for Memento Mori

We all know that our lifespans are finite. What most of us don't know is how long that life will be. We may have decades left, or only months, weeks or days. Although we may be able to accept the fact that we will die at a rational level, very few of us are likely to be able to allow the knowledge of our mortality to impact on how we feel and act on a daily basis. And yet that was precisely the aim of many of the ancient thinkers. The philosophers of classical antiquity, Eastern sages and Christian theologians devised numerous ways of making us remember that we have to die, and that everything we cherish is impermanent. Even for them, however, practising the art of *memento mori* was highly challenging. It is not a cognitive exercise. Instead, we have to learn to feel into and truly accept our finitude. If we are able to do so, we will find ourselves liberated to live our lives in a much more fulfilling way.

Traditionally, the arts tend to be better at activating emotions and impacting on the structure of our feelings than are philosophy or sermons. Memento mori was a very common trope in the Middle Ages and the Renaissance, when painters, sculptors and architects planted numerous visual reminders of our finitude in their works. Most frequently, these took the form of a skull and bones, but they also appeared in the shape of coffins, hourglasses, rotten fruit and wilting flowers. *Vanitas* art served the exclusive function of drawing attention to the matter of death. Medieval funerary art or still lifes, for example, show the transience of life, the short-lived futility of pleasure and beauty, and the ephemerality of wealth and earthly status.

The Stoic emperor Marcus Aurelius was fond of drawing attention to the vanity of all our desires. He constantly tried to remind himself of the impermanence of things, the flux and cyclical nature of change, and, of course, the great equaliser that is death. Aurelius was pretty cavalier about the end. Death, so what, he shrugged: 'You embarked, you set sail, you made port. Go ashore now. ... You should always look on human life as short and cheap. Yesterday sperm: tomorrow a mummy or ashes.'[1]

But while he was almost flippant about the inevitability of death, he took the lessons we should draw from that fact all the more seriously. It is precisely because our time is limited that we should not waste it, and instead treat it as a precious gift, making the most of every moment. The prospect of death can lend urgency to our actions and focus our attention on what really matters. Everything we do, say, or intend, should be like that of a dying person, Aurelius advises. We should not fear death, but rather fear never having begun to live according to our nature. In his *Letters from a Stoic*, Seneca writes: 'Let us prepare our minds as if we'd come to the very end of life. Let us postpone nothing. Let us balance life's books each day.' Seize the day, then, because time flies.

But how can we remember death on a daily basis, other than by getting a skull tattooed on our forehead, listening to funeral masses in B minor at full blast, putting rotten fruit on our desk and hanging out in graveyards? The answer is that we probably can't. Our finitude is a fact our conscious mind loves to repress, for it is a kind of knowledge that can be as disturbing as it might be energising. We could also not really live in a sustainable way with the intensity of purpose, focus and determination that the Stoics envisage. It would be too exhausting. It makes sense, therefore, that the Christian rites of Ash Wednesday, when we are urged to drop ashes on our head and recall that we are dust and that unto dust we shall return, are celebrated only once a year. The ritual would lose all its power were it to be a daily one. The same holds true for the Day of the Dead in Mexico, which is a much more cheerful and, paradoxically, life-affirming affair than its name suggests.

It can, however, be helpful to seek to shift perspective from time to time, to zoom out of our daily problems and to remember both the bigger picture and the broader timeline. What might we regret not having done when we are lying on our deathbed? What among all the things we do truly matters, in the long run? Our regrets can be a most instructive teacher, as Harriet Beecher Stowe knew well: 'The bitterest tears shed over graves are for words left unsaid and deeds left undone.' They can point us to what we care about most deeply.

A powerful psychological tool, designed to help us to focus on our true values, is the 'Imagine your own funeral' exercise. It invites us to envisage that event, and to reflect on what we would want our friends and family to say about us. For which inner qualities and actions do we wish to be remembered? We probably don't want our kids to stand next to our coffin and say that we were always stressed, never stopped working and found it incredibly hard to relax. We also probably wouldn't want them to say that the only time they ever saw us happy was when we had a glass of wine in our hand. Similarly, we may not wish to hear our parents lament that they were tremendously proud of us because we always paid our taxes on time and our boss thought highly of us, but that they hadn't seen us for years. And nor would we want our spouse to say that we were anxious most of the time, always planning the next steps and prepping for potential catastrophes, and that we didn't have much to give to others because we were so preoccupied our own worries. How, then, *do* we want to be remembered?

One of the great paradoxes of time, in my experience at least, is that the more of it we think we have, the more we tend to squander it. It is interesting that in myths and stories most beings who are gifted immortality actually tend to see eternal life not as a blessing but rather as a curse (the gods being the great exception, but then again we just don't know much about their inner lives). The Sibyl is one example: according to Greek legend, the prophetess asked Apollo for longevity, but forgot to ask for eternal youth. As the centuries passed, her body withered and grew so small that it was kept in a jar, until eventually only her voice was left. Vampires are another example. After a few centuries, most of the fanged undead are weary of the world and of life more generally: they long for an ending. Think Dracula and Louis in the film *Interview with the Vampire* (1994). A notable exception is Tilda Swinton's character Eve in Jim Jarmusch's film *Only Lovers Left Alive* (2013). Her morose partner Adam is a melancholic Romantic, a suicidal Goth who collects outdated technology and longs for eternal rest. Eve, by contrast, is a relentless seeker of knowledge: she amasses wisdom, and never tires of her immortality because there is always something new to learn, new books to read, new art to admire and a boundless supply of beauty to behold. But most of us are nothing like Eve. Generally speaking, we tend to appreciate that which is limited, rare and finite much more than that which is available in large quantities. The issue is that we tend to think and behave as if our lifetime falls into the latter category, when in fact it belongs firmly in the former.

In Psalm 90, Moses urges God to 'number our days that we may get a heart of wisdom'.[2] God duly did what Moses asked, but it didn't really make us any wiser. Christians do, of course, have the afterlife to look forward to. To them, earthly life is partly dress rehearsal, partly a try-out phase during which they hope to prove their moral calibre and qualify for re-admittance to Paradise. Those believing in rebirth and the cyclicality of all life, too, do not really think of their current lifespan as all there is. The pressure, however, is on for those of us who don't believe in a hereafter or in reincarnation. We really do have to make use of this one life we have right now – of whatever duration it may be.

As Eckhart Tolle reminds us in *The Power of Now: A Guide to Spiritual Enlightenment* (1997), the now is all we have and all we ever will have, so we should learn to cherish it. Most of us are not very good at that, though, for the majority of our thoughts and emotions revolve around the past or our future. We compulsively vacillate between memory and anticipation. Our past furnishes us with an identity, and narratives of cause and effect, while 'the future holds the promise of salvation, of fulfilment in whatever form'.[3] But both are illusions. The present moment is all we ever really possess. The now is not only the most precious thing there is, it is the only thing there is. And who knows for how much longer we will have our nows, for, after all, no one here gets out alive.

N is for Narratives

We may be forgiven for thinking that ours is the most exhausting period in history. Many of us look back nostalgically to times we imagine to have been less strenuous. We may dream of living in a bucolic age in which motor cars, fast food, social media, iPhones and neo-liberalism had not yet been invented. The truth, however, is that ours is far from being the only generation to have battled with the demons of exhaustion. Our ancestors, too, worried a great deal about exhaustion's effects on the mind, the body and the community. Ironically, they also often looked back to bygone golden ages in which they imagined life to have been simpler and better. Just like us, then, our ancestors felt that their times were particularly hard and wearying. And yet the narratives they told themselves about their exhaustion were very different from ours.

Ancient precursors of our modern-day exhaustion include melancholia, acedia and neurasthenia. All three share core symptoms with burnout and depression as we understand them today. These symptoms include lethargy, torpor, slowness and weakness, as well as irritability, hopelessness and pessimism. What is more, these older diagnoses can yield insights into then-prevalent anxieties. For the causes on which we pin our exhaustion are always revealing. The stories we tell about them show us what we tend to worry about at specific moments in history, and which social or technological developments we might view as particularly threatening to our way of life and to our mental and physical well-being.

Nowadays, we explain our exhaustion mainly as the consequence of chronic stress at work, social media and email, and the discontents of competitive individualism, including loneliness, the lack of a purpose that extends beyond ourselves and a lack of a sense of belonging. In the pre-modern period, by contrast, exhaustion was understood as the result of an imbalance of the humours and as a spiritual failing. Renaissance scholars associated exhaustion with scholarly activities and the alignment of the planets, especially Saturn's malign influence, while eighteenth-century medics deemed the 'solitary sin' of masturbation to be the main cause for our depleted energies. In the nineteenth century, exhaustion was widely understood as the consequence of too much brain work, a sensitive constitution and overstimulation.[1] What can we learn from these earlier ways of understanding exhaustion?

Melancholia is the oldest of the exhaustion-related diagnoses. First described by Hippocrates and Galen, it was understood as a combination of fear and causeless sorrow that results in dejection, lack of energy and misanthropy. Until the advent of modern medicine in the nineteenth century, most illnesses were thought to be the result of imbalances between the four bodily humours: blood, phlegm, yellow bile and black bile. To re-establish harmony between these humours, physicians used interventions such as bloodletting and purging. Melancholia was thought to be caused by a surplus of black bile. The ancient physicians imagined that the body sought to self-correct its out-of-kilter humoral economy by burning excessive quantities of black bile in the stomach. The ashes and fumes of the burnt bilious matter, however, rose from the lower regions of the body into the sufferer's head, where they quite literally clouded their judgement. The black soot made melancholics see themselves and the world through a darkened lens.

Melancholics were thought to be grumpy, rude, miserable and often misanthropic. They were probably the least popular of the four personality types – the others being cholerics, phlegmatics and the sanguine. However, melancholia was also associated with genius and creativity, and was often seen as a condition of the learned. The links between melancholia and exceptionality peaked in the Romantic period, when a bunch of rule-breaking and world-weary poets glamorised weariness in all its manifestations. But the association between melancholia and exceptionality is in fact much older. It can be traced back to Aristotle, who wondered why it was that 'all men who have become outstanding in philosophy, statesmanship, poetry or the arts are melancholic?'[2]

In the post-classical Christian period, melancholia was recast as acedia. Acedia is derived from the ancient Greek word for indifference, listlessness or apathy. It denotes a 'state of non-caring' and has been described as 'weariness of the heart'. Just like melancholia and burnout, it includes various symptoms of mental and physical exhaustion. Crucially, however, acedia was understood neither as an organic disease caused by humoral imbalances nor as a matter of personality type, but as a spiritual and moral failing. Theologians like Evagrius Ponticus (346–99 CE), John Cassian (360–435) and the thirteenth-century Italian scholar Thomas Aquinas (1225–74) considered acedia to be a sinful disease of the will. They thought it a sign of a weak or lacking faith. Even worse, acedia was understood as a form of existential ingratitude, even as contempt for God's divine creation.[3] Acedia was also associated with the 'noonday demon' who attacks when the heat is at its most oppressive.[4] Those lacking in faith were frequently compared to a pot of lukewarm milk on which flies settle readily.[5] They were considered rotten at the core.

In *The Monastic Institutes* (c. 425 CE), a practical handbook for monks, John Cassian argued that those in the grip of acedia feel disgust with their lifestyles and contempt for their fellow monks, which is reminiscent of 'depersonalisation', a core feature of burnout.[6] Acedia, he writes, makes the monk 'lazy and sluggish about all manner of work'.[7] Those suffering from acedia long to be elsewhere, are unable to read, to concentrate, to pray or to undertake any productive activity. Like burnouts, they suffer from brain fog and radically diminished efficacy. Around midday, the acedic monk experiences

> such bodily weariness and longing for food that he seems to himself worn out and wearied as if with a long journey, or some very heavy work, or as if he had put off taking food during a fast of two or three days. Then besides this he looks about anxiously this

way and that, and sighs that none of the brethren come to see him, and often goes in and out of his cell, and frequently gazes up at the sun, as if it was too slow in setting, and so a kind of unreasonable confusion of mind takes possession of him like some foul darkness, and makes him idle and useless for every spiritual work, so that he imagines that no cure for so terrible an attack can be found in anything except visiting some of the brethren, or in the solace of sleep alone.[8]

Here, Cassian describes the physical symptoms of acedia in terms of what we would now call post-exertion malaise, a bodily fatigue that is as intense as that experienced after prolonged fasting, hard labour or extended walking. He also describes the symptoms of hopelessness, restlessness, comfort eating and an inability to focus. Ultimately, the monk, 'worn out by the spirit of accidie, as by some strong battering ram', sinks into slumber or else seeks idle chit-chat with his fellow monks, but emerges from both activities even more exhausted.[9]

It's a classic vicious circle: the acedic become ever less able to meditate and to contemplate things of a spiritual nature, while their ill-chosen strategies for restoring their energy aggravate their condition further. In that sense, they are just like us – weary twenty-first-century burnouts who engage in a host of similarly unproductive displacement activities. Unable to concentrate on our tasks, we may check our email, Twitter or Instagram accounts, purchase pointless stuff online, seek distraction from our emptiness in food, drink or the constant company of others, or else succumb to feelings of hopelessness and despair.

Acedia is now much better known as the cardinal sin of sloth. In fact, sloth was considered the gravest of the Seven Deadly Sins – the vice that opened the door to all the others, giving rise to envy, gluttony, lust, wrath, pride and avarice. Geoffrey Chaucer's parson in *The Canterbury Tales* (1386–95) declares sloth to be 'the gate of all sins. An idle man is like a place without walls; the devil may enter on every side and shoot at him with temptations while he's unprotected.'[10] But what exactly was so alarming about sloth? Why were religious thinkers so preoccupied with the condition, which, compared to the other deadly sins, seems quite harmless in nature?

First, it is important to note that acedia emerged in monastic settings. In tight-knit communities such as monasteries, fairly distributed and clearly regulated labour matters. Generally speaking, the more complex our social structures become, the more those who do not contribute their share endanger the smooth functioning of the system. Not only does the success of the group depend on everyone performing their allocated role, but those who do not pull their weight also cause resentment. Such resentment can easily spiral. A prevailing sense of unfairness (whether justified or not) can pose a serious threat to social cohesion.[11] Just think of the toxic effects of colleagues who always wriggle out of their commitments and pass their work on to others. They can easily corrode the team's morale. The same is true of partners who do not take on their fair share of household chores. Think, too, of the hatred the British tabloid press enjoys whipping up about those on benefits, who are often characterised as scroungers or parasites.

The establishment of the canon of the Seven Deadly Sins, then, was driven not just by abstract theological reasoning but also by pragmatic social considerations. Sloth was so dangerous because it could breed resentment and prove to be harmful to the social fabric. The exhausted of our age pose a considerable economic and social risk, too. Sick leave as a result of stress, depression and burnout costs companies billions in lost revenue each year. The strain these conditions put on public health services continues to rise dramatically. The problem of burnout, then, doesn't just affect the individual but also impacts society and the body politic. It is therefore all the more important that its underlying structural causes are properly understood and addressed, and that the responsibility for burnout is not just seen as an individual problem.

The spectre of exhaustion raised its head once more in the nineteenth century, which saw rapid industrialisation, the spread of capitalism and the expansion of the middle classes. This time, exhaustion was understood as a core symptom of neurasthenia, a condition popularised in the early 1880s by the physician and electrotherapist George M. Beard.[12] Beard defined neurasthenia as 'nervous weakness', and a 'deficiency or lack of nerve force'.[13] Beard and his followers saw the brain as a kind of battery.[14] They believed that just like battery power, nerve force was limited in quantity and could easily be depleted if managed unwisely.

Beard certainly hit a nerve with his diagnosis and it spread rapidly. In the final decade of the nineteenth century, it was highly fashionable to be neurasthenic in America and Western Europe. Why was neurasthenia so popular? First, Beard clearly signposted neurasthenia as a physical rather than a psychological disorder. It was thus free of the stigma that tends to attach to mental health conditions. He also associated it firmly with the educated middle and upper classes, arguing that its symptoms were the result of too much 'brain work'. Neurasthenia, he writes, was particularly common among businessmen and captains of industry. He also suggested that only the sensitive and those with a 'fine organization' were capable of suffering from neurasthenia:

> The fine organization is distinguished from the coarse by fine, soft hair, delicate skin, nicely chiselled features, small bones, tapering extremities, and frequently by a muscular system comparatively small and feeble. It is frequently associated with superior intellect, and with a strong and active emotional nature. ... It is the organization of the civilized, refined and educated, rather than of the barbarous and low-born and untrained – of women more than of men. [15]

Classist, racist and sexist as it is, this description was, of course, highly flattering for those in the period who felt it represented them.

Most importantly, however, Beard declared neurasthenia a disease of civilisation, triggered by various phenomena of the modern age. The causes of neurasthenia were firmly attributed, then, to the outside world – to technological and social changes that drained the limited energy reserves of modern men and women. The modern environment, particularly cities, were thought to generate far too many exhausting stimuli. People's senses were incessantly assaulted by noise, sights and information. Beard worried that the sensitive nervous systems of men and women would simply be unable to cope with this continuous sensory overload.

All things considered, then, it is not at all surprising that neurasthenia became so fashionable, and that so many embraced the diagnosis with enthusiasm. Beard associated such positive and flattering qualities with the neurasthenic disposition that in effect he turned it into a distinction rather than a disease. Neurasthenia was a marker of evolutionary refinement and social and intellectual status, a condition signalling sensitivity, industriousness and sophistication. The diagnosis also relieved sufferers from personal responsibility for their exhaustion, because it was caused by factors firmly beyond their control. We can see a faint trace of these associations in some discussions of burnout and stress today. While burnout is no longer the badge of honour that it might once have been, it is still understood to mean that we have given our all, and more, to our work. It indicates that we are caring, conscientious and compassionate, and that we always put others first, heroically ignoring our own needs even if that eventually makes us ill. Being stressed also signals that we are important and in constant demand.

What can we learn from these examples from the long history of exhaustion? First, we can see that the narratives we construct about the causes of our exhaustion change through history, sometimes radically so. Secondly, the causes of our exhaustion shift between the physical and the psychological, the cultural and the technological, the internal and the external. And thirdly, these changing narratives also illustrate how we judge the exhausted – whether we hold them personally responsible for their condition or else consider them to be the victims of circumstances that are beyond their control. At some moments in its history, exhaustion was seen as a sign of intellectuality, sensitivity and sophistication.

At others, the exhausted were considered morally defective sinners, idlers and scroungers, and even as a grave threat to the social fabric. We should, then, reflect carefully on our own exhaustion narratives, and question the underlying assumptions about agency and responsibility in the stories we tell ourselves, as well as the moral judgements that tend to accompany them.

O is for Oblomov

Oblomov is the infamous anti-hero of the Russian writer Ivan Goncharov's eponymous novel, published in 1859.[1] He is best known for being an incorrigible slacker. We first encounter him wrapped in his threadbare Oriental dressing gown, refusing to get out of bed. His eyes glide wearily across the dusty objects in his derelict bedchamber. Around him, all is filth and cobwebs – his room hasn't been cleaned for years, and the plaster ceiling is crumbling. His servant repeatedly urges him to get up, to dress and to shave, but his efforts are in vain. So are those of a string of visitors who try to lure Oblomov from his bed and to convince him to step outside into the St Petersburg spring.

Oblomov's refusal to leave his bed and to live an active life becomes increasingly problematic. He has to vacate his apartment but can't muster the energy to look for an alternative; his estate in the countryside is decaying because of chronic neglect and mismanagement. His annual allowance runs out. Tricksters begin to prey on him, robbing him of money he doesn't even have. But in spite of the existentially threatening nature of his problems, Oblomov just can't rouse himself into action. Every day, he resolves to write letters to put his affairs in order, but never gets very far. Sometimes, he manages to put a few lines to paper, but then gets caught up in the vexing grammatical question of the difference between restrictive and non-restrictive clauses (in other words when to use 'which' and when to use 'that'). The letters are never finished and never sent, and his affairs deteriorate at an alarming pace.

Oblomov's friends repeatedly rescue him from bankruptcy, free him from the clutches of various financial exploiters, and do their best to rouse him from his state of inertia. Their efforts prove to be fruitless. He dies young, as a result of too much sleep, too much vodka, wine and red meat, and a lack of exercise. And yet, for all that, his life has not been an unhappy one. In his final years, he finds love, and many people genuinely care for him. Moreover, he has never been lazy merely in the sense of preferring rest to activity, and pleasure and leisure to work. Rather, he has serious philosophical reservations about the active life. As he puts it to his best friend, Stolz: 'All these society people are dead men, men fast asleep, they are worse than I am! What is their aim in life? They do not lie in bed like me, they dash backwards and forwards every day like flies, but what is the good?'[2] When Stolz accuses his friend of 'Oblomovism', a term he has invented to characterise Oblomov's turpitude and lack of ambition, Oblomov counters: 'Doesn't everyone strive for the very same things that I dream of? … isn't it the purpose of all your running about, your passions, wars, trade, politics – to secure rest, to attain this ideal of a lost paradise?'[3]

While the land-owning Oblomov, who has never worked a day in his life, symbolises the lethargy, paralysis and self-destructive trajectory of a dying feudal Russia, he also stands as a challenge to the values of work, self-improvement and productivity. He questions the merit of progress, and instead dreams of an earthly paradise where it is not necessary to work, and where, in place of milk and honey, there is plenty of vodka.

While he may appear to be a mainly negative figure, an example of what we should all avoid, Oblomov's views warrant serious consideration in the context of psychoanalyst Josh Cohen's distinction between slackers, slobs and burnouts. Cohen identifies Snoopy, Garfield, Homer Simpson and the Big Lebowski as slobs in the sense that they are 'dissidents from the imperative of productivity'.[4] As Cohen explains, slobs differ in a crucial way from those who are burnt out: 'Unlike the burnout, whose enjoyment of lassitude is spoiled by nervous agitation, shame and guilt, the scandalous courage of the slob embraces the inertial state, and rejects openly the diligence and responsibility that confer full social legitimacy in a culture defined by work and productivity.'[5] In other words, slobs celebrate their laziness, they love to shock and to provoke disgust, and they enjoy their outsider status. The slob rejects dominant cultural values, in particular the idea that we have to work, to be useful and to be productive. They are a thorn in the flesh of the hard-working, mocking their commitment and modelling a completely different kind of life.

Oblomov, however, is more slacker than slob. He doesn't aim to cause offence, he doesn't brag. Importantly, he manages to get ever better at enjoying his life. In his final years, he no longer feels guilt and no longer has a nagging desire to change his ways – largely because he has found a woman who loves him as he is and who has become his full-time carer, managing all the practicalities of existence in his stead. In contrast, at the beginning of the novel, his key challenge is procrastination. He is plagued by guilt and anxiety, he feels like he should work, he knows he has to work, but he simply can't. He has big ideas about what he wants to do with his life and how to fix his estate, and yet he never gets round to translating any of them into action. Not ever managing to start what we most care about is, ironically, exactly the point of procrastination.

Procrastination, Oliver Burkeman suggests, is a way of maintaining a 'feeling of omnipotent control over life – because you needn't risk the upsetting experience of failing at an intimidating project, obviously, if you never even start it'.[6] When we procrastinate, we remain firmly anchored in the realm of possibility. We don't narrow down our idea of the future, with all its shimmering possibilities. By procrastinating, we try to keep all our options open. We preserve the fantasy of optionality. For it is often the crushing gap between the ideal and the real that keeps procrastinators from doing anything. They care so much about their vision that they fear the inevitable imperfections of reality. While they may be avoiders in practice, procrastinators are theoretical perfectionists.

Many of us tend to postpone the tasks we most care about. This is a tendency I see in myself and in many of my clients. We live in a 'When Then' state of mind: when I have got this or that out of the way, when I have gained my degree, finished this project, found the perfect partner, lost weight, feel less stressed at work ... *then* I will do x. That means that many of us never get started on what matters most to us. We spend our time trying to get all the tasks that don't matter but have to be done out of the way, so that we will be free, one day, to work on what really does matter to us. But logically, we have it exactly the wrong way round. Burkeman argues that we should always work on our most important projects first, not last. He recommends that we dedicate to that which matters most to us at least the first good hour of each day. We need to reverse our thinking, tackle what we genuinely care about first, and then do what we have to do afterwards. That means prioritising, not delaying, writing that novel, meditating, running, learning Japanese, setting up our own business, investing more time in relationships, breeding Siamese cats, travelling the world, or learning to sail.

The American businessman and philanthropist Warren Buffett, too, highlights the dangers of middling priorities. He isn't interested in curing slobs or slackers such as Oblomov. Rather, he wants to help diligent and motivated people who suffer from getting their priorities wrong. He argues that, if we want to live our lives well, we should make a list of twenty-five things that matter most to us in life, with the most important first. Then, we should focus only on the first five. And rather than keeping the other twenty in the background, as optional/additional items to which we might return when we have extra time, we should avoid spending any time on them at all. Why? According to Buffett, the middling priorities are where the real danger lies – for they are the most potent distractors from our key life goals. That is because we also want to dedicate time to them, and thus we spread ourselves too thinly. Furthermore, it is often much easier to work on what matters less, because what matters most is so highly charged, and the thought of failing at it can be existentially threatening.

Oblomov is a creature of the in-between, as are many of us, to a greater or lesser extent. Half troubled procrastinator, half passionate philosopher of rest, he has two impulses battling for his soul. On the one hand, he feels a desire to shake off his stupor and join the army of the active, to be a master of his own affairs and put an end to his dependency on the kindness of his friends. On the other hand, he is a willing slave to the pleasure principle and also to the death drive – according to Freud, our desire to return to an inanimate state – and he sees beauty in both. He heeds the siren call of stillness and sleep. Yet by renouncing all work, all effort, all inconvenience and risk, he practises a kind of death in life, eliminating many of the things that make life worth living. There is much to learn from him as we seek to lift ourselves out of that in-between place where we can never really achieve anything meaningful.

P is for Perfectionism

I see the best minds of my generation – including many of my clients – lost to perfectionism. So what, we may shrug. Isn't perfectionism essentially a good thing, a socially sanctioned and ultimately useful form of striving for excellence? Unfortunately, it is not that simple. Perfectionism is very much a double-edged sword. It has many positive effects, but it can also pose serious challenges to our mental and physical health. Wishing to do the things we do as well as we can is an unequivocally positive desire. The same is true for the appreciation of excellence. Both are expressions of care and conscientiousness. They are also related to the admiration of quality and beauty – for excellence is their close cousin. We can understand excellence as beauty in action, as a form of applied or enacted splendour. However, our appreciation of excellence can also morph into an unhealthy and debilitating struggle to achieve perfection at all costs. It can lead to us castigating ourselves very harshly for our perceived imperfections, and to spending far too much time and energy on our tasks. Perfectionism, moreover, can be a significant driver of burnout.

Perfectionism is commonly understood as a personality disposition. Perfectionists aspire to the condition of faultlessness and unsurprisingly tend to have excessively high standards for their own performance. Etymologically, perfectionism is related to the notion of completion. But ironically, many perfectionists find it very hard to let go of their work, to accept that it is as good as it can reasonably be. We fear the moment when we have to say, that's it, and face the many ways in which our efforts may have fallen short of our ideals. As soon as we declare our work finished, it has moved from the realm of possibility and theoretical perfection into the sphere of actuality, in which genuine perfection remains rare.

We can see perfectionism as a positive desire always to produce the most flawless version of something. But perfection can also become a mirage that we chase in vain. We can set ourselves such unreachably high standards for our own work that we will never be able to meet them, no matter how hard we try, and thus we are setting ourselves up to fail. Perfectionism can also be misplaced. My grandfather was a carpenter. He was so obsessed with making every one of his pieces perfect that he simply took far too long to complete any of them. His clients grew frustrated with the delays. But my grandfather just could not bring himself to let go of any of his pieces until his inner perfectionist was satisfied. Eventually, this tendency cost him his business. If he had been a bespoke furniture maker, his perfectionism and attention to detail would probably have served him well. But what he actually made was equipment for farmers. They really just wanted sturdy wagons in which they could transport their hay from A to B. They didn't care about any of the many beautifully thought-through, flawlessly executed details into which my grandfather had poured his heart. They wanted functional products, delivered at a reasonable speed and at a reasonable price.

How, then, can we differentiate between valuing excellence and counterproductive perfectionism? What exactly is it that makes perfectionism so dangerous? The psychologists Joachim Stoeber and Lavinia E. Damian have proposed a helpful model. They differentiate between 'perfectionist striving' (that is, the desire to deliver excellent work and perform at the highest possible standard) and what they call 'perfectionist concerns'.[1] This distinction is key. For the worm in the apple of perfectionism really is perfectionist concerns. Stoeber and Damian understand perfectionist concerns broadly as negative assessments of our own performance – the inner judgements we make after we have completed a task. These assessments are usually associated with anxieties about having made mistakes, fears about being judged negatively by others and disappointment about the gap between our vision and our actual performance.[2]

Perfectionist concerns about our own performance are typically associated with neuroticism, avoidance behaviour and negative feelings and thoughts. Perfectionist strivings, by contrast, are associated mainly with positives, including conscientiousness, problem-solving and enjoyable emotions. Perfectionist striving, then, has highly positive effects and can help us thrive and learn.[3] In plainer language, perfectionism's psychological dangers are located in our own overly critical evaluation of our performance. Research has also shown that perfectionists have a lower tolerance for ambiguity. Alongside flawlessness, it seems, we also crave certainty. That, combined with our often absurdly high standards, can, ironically, make us both less productive and less efficient at work.[4]

The School of Life collective takes a psychoanalytical view of the matter. It deems that perfectionism has its roots in self-hatred, in an abiding feeling that we are not good enough, unworthy and flawed. It considers our striving for perfection at work and elsewhere as an attempt to over-come an early deficit in love which manifests in an abiding feeling of lack. 'We aren't interested in perfect work at all', they write: 'We are trying to escape from a feeling of being awful people, and work simply happens to be the medium through which we strive to grow tolerable in our own eyes.'[5] When we strive for perfection, all we want is to feel acceptable. But because the quality of our work was never the actual problem, it can also never be the solution.

There are five key reasons why perfectionism of the evaluative kind is dangerous and can make us ill. First, perfectionistic judgements are associated with negative self-talk and harsh verdicts on our performance. Our inner perfectionist can easily turn into an inner critic, even an inner saboteur or torturer. If we lack self-compassion and a healthy appreciation of our own skills, constantly drag-ging our own achievements and accomplishments into the mud, our inner life will become a major stressor in its own right. We can become our own worst enemy.

Secondly, perfectionists don't just strive for high per-formance, they also have an unhealthy relationship with mistakes. We do not tend to see mistakes as teachers or as a learning opportunity, but live in constant fear of failure and negative reactions from others to our perceived imperfection.[6] In other words – and again, ironically – although we strive for perfection, we often tend not to have a growth mindset. We admonish ourselves terribly for any perceived failures and also fear punishment by others. That tendency can be so strong that we resort to avoidance behaviour. Sometimes, we refuse to let go of our work because we are not happy with it, or else we won't even get started on our projects. We may become endlessly procrastinating armchair perfectionists, so fearful of failure that we decide to remain permanently in the realm of possibility. And this is not surprising when the stakes are so high, when each task we engage in essentially becomes a 'referendum on our legitimacy'.[7]

Thirdly, perfectionists also have a tendency to worry and ruminate unproductively about work. This aspect of perfectionism in particular can lead to exhaustion or even burnout. We find it really difficult, often even impossible, to switch off from our tasks. Work-related anxieties tend to intrude into our leisure time. This proclivity negatively affects our work–life balance, our health and our overall well-being.[8] And when we do complete our tasks, we can only see what hasn't worked well, rather than acknowledging what has. We don't celebrate our achievements, and simply hasten on to the next chore.

Fourthly, perfectionism often goes hand in hand with workaholism. Workaholism is defined as an excessive need to work that interferes with our bodily health, personal happiness and interpersonal relations. It is associated with low levels of psychological well-being and high levels of emotional distress. Workaholism can have a seriously negative impact on our health and longevity because workaholics tend not to get enough leisure time, exercise or sleep.[9] In other words, workaholism is pretty ruinous at all levels – mentally, physically and socially. Only a few decades ago, workaholism and its dangers loomed large in the cultural imagination. Nowadays, it has almost vanished from our vocabulary. Could that be because workaholism is now the norm rather than the exception? Like the air we breathe, we don't even see it. Given that our work–life balance is a powerful indicator of our individual health and well-being, this is a deeply unsettling thought.[10]

And finally, for all of these reasons combined, perfectionists are also at a much higher risk of burnout.[11] Perfectionism drives us to work harder, or even to work all the time, to judge what we do and achieve harshly, to be unable to stop thinking about our work and to live in fear of negative assessments or even punishment from others for our perceived failings. It can thus lead to extreme physical and emotional exhaustion, diminished personal efficacy and a loss of faith in our ability to do our jobs at all.

If we dive deeper to explore the origins of our perfectionism, we will probably find that evaluative perfectionism has its roots in our childhoods. Most perfectionists are likely to have had parents with high standards. Some of us might even have been made to feel that we were never good enough. We may also have received a kind of love that was conditional on achievement. What is more, we often tend to internalise overly critical voices from our past, which can become quite dangerous to our health and emotional well-being later in life.

But perfectionism is not only an individual ailment. It is also a consequence of a wider cultural malaise. Perfectionism is the upshot of a society based on the principle of competition. Simply put, what is most perfect and functional tends to win. Our perfectionist culture is one in which we are encouraged and expected to cherish that which is flawless, seamless and smooth, and to fear imperfection of all kinds, especially in the form of ageing, vulnerability and dysfunction. Aspiring to the aesthetics of the artificial, we photoshop and filter our own perceived flaws. And we forget that beauty can also be found in the crooked and the blemished.

The Japanese know this well. They tend to appreciate the power of an irregular, knotty tree branch in an otherwise flawless minimalist setting. They appreciate the effect of a piece of driftwood on perfectly polished parquet, and of the beauty spot placed in an otherwise symmetrical face. Most importantly, they celebrate the art of *kintsugi*. Kintsugi entails mending broken ceramics with a clearly visible, golden-lacquered glue. It is precisely in their shimmering scars where their beauty resides. Their repaired brokenness renders them unique and human, reminding us of our own imperfections and fragility. 'Imperfection', the Buddhist psychologist Tara Brach writes, 'is not our personal problem – it is a natural part of existing. We all get caught in wants and fears, we all act unconsciously, we all get diseased and deteriorate.'[12]

How, then, can we disempower our inner perfectionist

in such a way that we keep its positive qualities and energies alive? Might it be possible for us to have our perfectionist cake and eat it, in other words, to find a way to switch off our evaluative perfectionism only? Is it possible to strive for excellence both in theory and in practice but to avoid judging ourselves too harshly if we don't achieve it? If there is hope, then it lies in our embracing a paradox and learning to become, to paraphrase Donald Winnicott, 'good enough' perfectionists. We would become perfectionists who genuinely try our best but are gentle and forgiving with ourselves about the often less-than-perfect results of our efforts. We would be perfectionists who recognise that in the gap between our own high standards and our abilities, a crooked kind of beauty may reside, just as it does in the golden glue of a mended vase.

Q is for Qi

While Western medicine tends to focus on treating illnesses, Traditional Chinese Medicine (TCM) devotes its energies primarily to prevention rather than cure. Furthermore, practitioners of TCM take a systemic, holistic approach to well-being. They consider it absurd to look at symptoms in isolation. In their view, everything is connected: the mind and the body, the individual and the social, the microcosm and the macrocosm.

Both in a moral and in a medical sense, Chinese thought emphasises the importance of self-cultivation. It encourages us to think of the self as a garden that needs to be cultivated with care and attention. Ultimately, we are responsible for what grows in our patch. It is up to us to manage the sowing, watering, weeding, pruning and harvesting. We need to make sure there is biodiversity and balance, and that we don't exhaust the soil. Encouraging a slow and steady approach to fostering sustainable good habits, Chinese medicine promotes lifestyles that avoid physical illness as well as major mental and spiritual disturbances. Moreover, Chinese medical and philosophical texts conceive of us as profoundly relational creatures who are bound up with each other and our environments, and deeply embedded in social and cosmological frameworks. But nowhere is the difference between Western and Chinese approaches to well-being more apparent than in their respective attitudes to energy. While a detailed conception of human energy is absent from Western biomedical accounts (see 'E is for Energy'), energy is the most central category in TCM. Why is that the case? And what can we learn from ancient Chinese wisdom on that matter?

TCM is less concerned with establishing relations of cause and effect, and with looking at diseases in isolation, than with focusing on patterns. Above all, it seeks to restore balance and harmony in the body, as well as between the social, physical, mental and cosmic domains. The key strategy for restoring balance in our lives is ensuring the healthy flow of *qi*. Qi has been translated as 'air', 'breath', 'vapour', 'spirit', 'elemental force' and 'vital energy'. It is our life force and also the quality that enables all change. The ancient Chinese ideogram for qi consisted of three horizontal strokes that symbolise cloudlike vapour, like breath becoming visible on a cold day.[1] The ideogram has also been understood as representing a ritual prayer that comes from below and rises to the heavens, or as cooked rice from which steam emerges.[2] The qi ideogram thus evokes those most essential human energy suppliers, air and food, both in their mundane and in their spiritual forms. It also suggests the ideas of movement, heat and transformation.

The Chinese assume that there are three basic kinds of qi. First, there is 'original qi', which is our inherited quantity of energy. It is passed on by parents to their children. Second, there is 'grain qi', which is the energy derived from food. Finally, there is 'natural air qi', which is extracted from the air we breathe.[3] These three types of qi broadly map onto Western ideas of genetics, diet and environment as vital factors that determine our well-being and energy levels. There are four major types of qi disharmonies: deficient qi, collapsed qi, stagnant qi and rebellious qi. When our qi is deficient or stagnant, we might suffer from inactivity, lack of tension and excessive stillness. Other symptoms might entail weakness or lethargy, and a sense of being blocked, frustrated, tense or moody.[4] Rebellious qi makes us confused, erratic and capricious.

In *The Yellow Emperor's Classic of Medicine* (c. 300–100 BCE), the Chinese equivalent of the Hippocratic corpus, these qi disharmonies and the interplay between the mind and the body are described as follows:

[M]any diseases come from disharmony of the qi. They often involve emotional disharmony. For example, when one is angry, the qi rises upward; when one is joyous, the qi disperses; when one is sad, the qi becomes exhausted; when one is fearful and frightened, the qi descends; when one is chilled, the qi contracts; when one is hot, the qi escapes; when one is anxious, the qi scatters and becomes chaotic; when one overstrains, the qi depletes; when one worries too much, the qi stagnates.[5]

Over-worrying 'draws too much qi to the spirit; the qi then does not perform its function of dispersing to other parts of the body. This results in congealing or stagnation of the qi.'[6] Concentration and the avoidance of emotional extremes, by contrast, can foster and preserve mental energy.

The Chinese imagine that qi travels through our bodies in 'meridians' or channels through which substances can flow, like our blood. Together with herbology, massage, and physical and breathing exercises, acupuncture is one of the primary therapeutics in Chinese Medicine. It is based on the idea that specific points on the surface of our body can influence what is happening on the inside. The aim of acupuncture is to tap into core meridians, or points where many meridians meet, to unblock stagnant qi, or else drain excessive qi or calm rebellious qi. In that sense, acupuncture is like the practice of bloodletting in humoral medicine, which was also designed to restore balance and harmony between the four bodily humours. Qi, however, is an invisible force, and acupunctural needles are only skin-deep. And while bloodletting was entirely counterproductive to restoring health, many people find acupuncture to be effective.

So, how can learning about qi help us overcome our present-day exhaustion? First, it is a reminder that there are other narratives and therapeutic models out there. The Western medical model has its blind-spots, and contemplating alternative cures for our ailments can be enriching. Acupuncture is an ancient practice that has survived for millennia because it continues to be effective for some physical ailments, and it has helped many who could not be cured through conventional Western methods. While we do not have to believe in the underlying explanation of acupuncture's effectiveness, we have nothing to lose by trying it. If acupuncture were a dud, it would have disappeared by now. The same holds true for many other ancient, energy-centred therapeutic approaches, such as yoga, qi gong and reiki. Moreover, simply choosing to do something for ourselves, spending time relaxing and focussing on our well-being and reframing how we think about our bodies and minds can sometimes have powerful benefits.

Second, the example of Chinese medicine and qi beautifully illustrates the ways in which our conceptions of what is going on in our bodies are shaped by our broader cultural imagination. The way we picture our bodies and energies, and how the mind, body and social interact, differs from culture to culture. In the West, the emphasis is often on evidence-based science and the empirical laws of physics, chemistry and biology. And that serves us well in many respects. But it also comes at a price: that which cannot be measured, quantified and seen, for example, tends to remain understudied or else is dismissed as pseudo-science. Human energy is a good example. What is more, a science-based world-view can be sterile, and does not offer us persuasive stories, imagery and rituals. It has significantly contributed to what the sociologist Max Weber called the 'disenchantment of the world' – the result of a general process of rationalisation and secularisation, which eradicated many forms of spirituality and communality that can offer rich and important ways of understanding what it is to be human. Perhaps most importantly, our scientific world-view tends to look at things in isolation, and often lacks viable frameworks for studying patterns, connections and the interplay of complex systems.

Q is for Qi

In Chinese medicine and philosophy, the microcosm and the macrocosm are thought to mirror one another. It is believed that external changes, such as geographic and seasonal ones, impact on internal changes, including our energy levels and feelings. Because everything is connected, the energy flow of the universe stimulates or subdues the life force of the individual. *The Yellow Emperor's Classic* states:

> Health and well-being can be achieved only by remaining centered in spirit, guarding against the squandering of energy, promoting the constant flow of qi and blood, maintaining harmonious balance of yin and yang, adapting to the changing seasonal and yearly macrocosmic influences, and nourishing one's self preventively.[7]

If we ignore the cyclical rise and fall of heavenly and elemental energies, we may harm our own supplies, for the qi of the human body flows in concert with that of the heavens and the earth.[8] In the West, we try to capture this relationship under the label of seasonal affective disorder, but compared to the Chinese conception of the entanglement of the micro with the macro it remains an impoverished concept. *The Yellow Emperor's Classic* proclaims: 'I have heard that one who understands the heavens will also understand people. One who understands ancient times shall understand the present. One who has a firm grasp of energy transformations will also understand the myriad things.'[9]

Last but not least, the idea of qi shows us how the ways in which we imagine our bodies – their functions, their organs and how they are connected – can be shaped by wider geographic conditions and social practices. The ancient Chinese empire was vast, dominated by great plains. The fourth and third centuries before the common era saw the launch of grand-scale wall-building, river irrigation and water-conservation projects.[10] The imagery of transportation systems, complex channels and unhindered movement and circulation of resources took on a prominent place in the Chinese cultural imagination. Notions of flow and stagnation, storage and conservation, defence and effective administration similarly loomed large in ancient Chinese culture.[11] Perhaps most importantly, the sheer scale of many Chinese projects required a sophisticated form of collaboration: the cultivation of the sprawling land, the establishment of comprehensive waterworks and especially the growing of rice – a notoriously difficult crop – had to be collective endeavours. This may be one of the reasons for the dominance of collectivist values over individualist ones in China, and the wider importance of maintaining social harmony, at whatever cost.[12] People simply had to work well together to survive. They had to develop complex social systems in which the welfare of the group took on a central place.

We can, then, trace the origins of the dominant medical metaphors and images of depletion, circulation and transportation, of harmony and imbalance, as well as notions of flow, stagnation and blockage, back to the ancient Chinese landscape, its unique agricultural traditions and social structures. In turn, we may wonder how our own culture and geography have shaped our perception of energy, of what depletes it and how we may restore it. In the Western imagination, depleted batteries, overdrawn bank accounts, overloaded or mis-wired computers tend to dominate. But are these mechanistic and financial metaphors genuinely helpful? May it not be more beneficial to adopt once again more nature-based imagery – given that we are nothing like isolated machines, but complex organic systems that are embedded, encultured and embodied? We, too, are likely to be profoundly shaped by our relationships, our environments, the seasons and many other forces the complex interplay of which we cannot yet fully understand.

R is for Rest

Rest is a state that is characterised by the cessation of work of any kind. It furnishes our lives with rhythm, not just in our waking and sleeping patterns but also in the way we structure our weeks by distinguishing between workdays and weekends, and by punctuating longer periods of work with holidays. It is a necessary counterpoint to human activity, during which we recover both physically and mentally from life's exertions. Rest is also a sensible response to the body's warning signals – be they tiredness, exhaustion, irritability or aching muscles.

The problem is that many of us have unlearned the ancient art of resting. Partly this is because we live in an age that fetishises productivity, speed and busyness. Resting is only tolerated as a necessary pause so that we can recuperate our energies and return to work. When we are trapped in a state of chronic exhaustion or burnout, unable either to work or properly to rest, our inability to rest becomes particularly dangerous. Burnout is often a catch-22 predicament. Because we have fallen behind with our work and feel anxious and guilty about that situation, we deny ourselves rest; but because we don't rest, our ability to work diminishes even more.

Before the advent of gas lamps and electricity in the nineteenth century, our time was largely structured by nature's rhythm. Working hours ended with the setting of the sun. The seasons dictated periods of intense activity at certain points in the year, such as during planting and harvest. These alternated with phases of relative inactivity – the cold winter months during which nature itself rests and nothing grows. The work of fishermen was orchestrated by the movements of the tide, and that of hunters followed the growth cycles and movements of their prey. Importantly, the natural patterns of rest and activity were communal – people worked and paused at the same time and celebrated holy days and harvest festivals together.

When clock time and artificial lighting were introduced, the pace and rhythm of work began to change. With the advent of factories and production lines in the industrial age, workers' rhythms were increasingly dictated by non-natural external factors. Frederick Winslow Taylor and Henry Ford tried systematically to optimise the pattern of their workers' rhythm of rest and motion to maximise output while avoiding expensive industrial accidents. Ford famously sought to enhance efficiency in his factories by eliminating unnecessary movements in the workers tasked with servicing his conveyor-belts. While Ford thus managed significantly to whittle down the production time for his motor cars, he also kept losing his workforce, whose discontent grew in tandem with the unyielding, externally imposed pace. They quit in droves.

The human need for rest was taken more seriously in the past. This is evident in the fact that the Sabbath rule features so prominently in the Ten Commandments, for example. The Ten Commandments is a list featuring only the most important of laws, including those proscribing murder, theft, adultery, jealousy, and blasphemy. The fourth of the commandments states:

> Remember the sabbath day, to keep it holy.
> Six days shalt thou labour, and do all thy work:
> But the seventh day *is* the sabbath of the Lord thy God:
> *in it* thou shalt not do any work, thou, nor thy son, nor
> thy daughter, thy manservant, nor thy maidservant,
> nor thy cattle, nor thy stranger that *is* within thy gates:
> For *in* six days the Lord made heaven and earth, the
> sea, and all that in them *is*, and rested the seventh day:
> wherefore the Lord blessed the Sabbath day, and hallowed it.[1]

Even the almighty and omnipotent God, it seems, needed a break after having created the heavens and the earth. The importance of rest in biblical times, however, was not motivated by the desire to enhance people's productivity, which is the primary modern justification of rest. Rather, it served the function of strengthening communal ties. When everyone rests on the same day, rest becomes an experience that brings people together, imposing a shared rhythm on their lives.[2]

The Jewish Sabbath tradition is the most serious attempt to honour the injunction to rest as a collective. It shows that it takes considerable effort, preparation and dedication to stop working at the same time. It needs to be insisted upon. There is, for example, a special Shabbat elevator in some Orthodox Jewish residences which operates without anyone having to press a button, for the use of technology is forbidden. Also prohibited is carrying and finishing things, cooking and washing, as well as a long list of more obviously work-like activities.

I will never forget my visit to the Outer Hebrides, a group of Scottish islands where a form of hard-core Calvinism still shapes various cultural practices. The isles of Lewis and Harris are the last bastions of Sabbath observance in the UK. There is strictly no work, no shopping and no form of transportation allowed on that day. No buses and ferries operate; any cars on the roads must head towards church. Most striking to me was the image of a playground near Stornoway: ardent Sabbatarians had meticulously locked up every single swing, so that no child could use them on the holy day. All of these examples illustrate the difficulty of distinguishing between what does and does not constitute work, although most people would probably not put swinging in the latter category. And while locking up swings seems a particularly joyless interpretation of honouring the Sabbath, we can say that it does show an earnest commitment to enforcing inactivity to make space for something else – spiritual contemplation.

In our age of 24/7 commerce, in which the market never sleeps, we have seen the erosion of communal resting times. We can now shop non-stop online and, in most countries, also in person. Sunday and lunchtime shop closures are a thing of the past, except in very hot countries with a siesta culture. As a consequence, in the West we have become increasingly desynchronised and fractured as a society. Many of us are now working and resting in different, highly personal time-zone bubbles. We rarely have a proper lunch break with colleagues, many of us working from home or having a quick sandwich between meetings in front of our screens. In the UK and the US, there is no collective tradition of a shared pause in summer during which everyone is out of the office and at the beach, as, for example, there is in France in August, when the entire country is on *les grandes vacances*.

Periods of rest, then, are highly important for fostering cohesive communities. It is also fair to say that if we don't rest well, the impact on our health and even our life expectancy can be severe. The neuroscientist Matthew Walker has shown how dangerous poor sleeping is for our overall health and mental well-being. Sleep, he argues, is more important for our health than diet, exercise or wealth.[3] The same holds true for rest. Rest's opposite is chronic stress, which can have major detrimental impacts on our health. The chronically stressed are likely to experience psychological distress and a range of serious health conditions, such as autoimmune disease, inflammation and coronary heart disease.[4]

The writer Robert Poynton advocates the importance of pausing in our lives.[5] Pauses, he argues, can facilitate creativity, stimulate serendipity and insight, and provide a way to push back against the expectation to be relentlessly productive. Pauses can be long or short; we may choose to take a breath or else a year-long sabbatical. By consciously introducing pauses into our routines, we can take back at least some control over the rhythms of our life and work. There is value in gaps and spaces, for they can function as a kind of creative opening. Well-placed pauses can be pregnant with meaning, and in music it is the pause which lends pieces their shape and beauty. But being able to pause requires the ability to stop doing what we are doing. And that is by no means easy.

Many people, Charles Darwin and present-day disciples of various time-management and productivity-enhancement techniques included, adhere to strict regimes of timed activity that alternate with regular pauses. Darwin, who suffered from low energy and chronic fatigue, took ample breaks during his workday, during which he would go for walks, snooze, have people read his correspondence or the news to him, or else dangle in a hammock on board the *Beagle*. He also scheduled longer periods of rest in spas where he took the waters.

Others who, be it through illness or overwork, also need to manage their energies more deliberately, have devised similar tailored patterns of activity and rest that work best for them. In the late 1980s, Francesco Cirillo developed the Pomodoro technique – a time-management method that breaks work into manageable intervals, typically about twenty-five minutes in length, which are followed by a short break of five to ten minutes. Cirillo used a tomato-shaped kitchen timer to set these intervals, and refers to each unit of work as a 'pomodoro' (the Italian word for tomato). He found that his method enabled him to learn and work much more effectively. To this day he has many ardent followers. When we devise our own regimes, however, it is essential not just to follow somebody else's method, but to base ours on a deep understanding of our unique rhythms.

When do our energies tend to peak and slump? When are we at our most alert? Do we work best in the morning or the evening, and after how many minutes or hours do we tend to need a break? There is simply no one-size-fits-all formula when it comes to rest.

Rest tends to be prescribed not only when we are exhausted but also when we are ill. However, there are different kinds of rest, some far better for us than others. The influential nineteenth-century American physician Silas Weir Mitchell put rest centre-stage in his therapeutics, and devised what became known as the 'rest cure'. This infamous cure required the patient's complete isolation, strict bed rest, deprivation of any intellectual stimuli and rapid weight gain.[6] His patients, the majority of whom were women, were confined to bed for a period of six to eight weeks. During this period of enforced rest, they also had to consume large quantities of milk (at least four pints a day) and mutton chops. Unsurprisingly, most were not big fans of this treatment, and its benefits were questionable. The powerful and disturbing short story 'The Yellow Wallpaper' (1892) by Charlotte Perkins Gilman reveals how it could be misused, being forced upon a woman as a kind of imprisonment that eventually drives her mad.

His dubious methods notwithstanding, Weir Mitchell put his finger on one of the great paradoxes when it comes to rest: the core symptom of the overworked brain is that it becomes unable to rest. Instead, it becomes literally restless. Often, this restlessness impacts on our ability to sleep. It's a classic vicious circle:

At last we stop and propose to find rest in bed. Not so, says the ill-used brain, now morbidly awake; and whether we will or not, the mind keeps turning over and over the work of the day, the business or legal problem, or mumbling, so to speak, some wearisome question in a fashion made useless by the denial of full attention. Or else the imagination soars away with the unrestful energy of a demon, conjuring up an endless procession of broken images and disconnected thoughts, so that sleep is utterly banished.[7]

How, then, can we rest well? In 2015, researchers from Durham University launched a 'Rest Test', in which more than 18,000 people from 134 countries participated. Respondents were asked to list what they found most restful. The top ten restful activities that emerged included reading, spending time in nature, being alone, listening to music, doing nothing much at all, taking a walk, having a bath, daydreaming, watching TV and practising mindfulness.[8] Intriguingly, five items from this list – seeking solitude, spending time in nature, walking, meditating and daydreaming – were also high on the agenda of the eighteenth-century philosopher Jean-Jacques Rousseau. Rousseau was one of the first Western thinkers to propose a return to nature as an antidote to the many stressors of modern life. To counter the growing sense of alienation in modern urban societies, he suggested in his *Reveries of the Solitary Walker* (1782), we must re-embrace nature and let both our feet and our minds wander, preferably in solitude.

The Italian expression *dolce far niente* captures the

sweet pleasantness of doing nothing and simply *being*. But for Rousseau, perambulating freely through woods and fields was also a way to connect with his authentic self. In particular, he worshipped nature's awe-inspiring beauty and its ability to remind us that we are but a tiny part of a larger whole. As other Romantic thinkers have also emphasised, when we are confronted with the sublimity of nature, we realise our own insignificance. Nature, in other words, can be a powerfully humbling force. It puts our sorrows into perspective.[9]

Rousseau also cherishes the powers of solitude. Only alone does he feel able to commune with his own thoughts, liberated from any requirement to conform to social conventions. By walking unobserved, surrounded only by plants and animals, he feels the lifting of a burden. Is it any surprise I love solitude so, Rousseau asks, when 'I see only animosity on men's faces, and nature always smiles at me'?[10] Yet it is not just the natural setting and the absence of hostile contemporaries, but also the act of walking itself which Rousseau deems so restorative. He is not alone in believing that solitary physical movement allows the mind to move as well, by indulging in a similar kind of non-goal-orientated ambulation. 'Solitude, I'll walk with thee', writes the poet John Clare, while his colleague William Wordsworth has immortalised the idea of wandering 'lonely as a cloud'. And Wordsworth practised what he preached: it is estimated that the poet walked 180,000 miles during his lifetime.

There is a lot we can learn from the Romantics' playbook, and especially when it comes to the topic of spiritual recuperation. 'Nature cure' self-help has been trending in the last two decades, urging us to rewild ourselves, to go forest bathing, cold-water swimming and birdwatching, to haunt urban parks, or simply potter around more in our gardens.[11] The Romantics' emphasis on solitude and on countering mental stress by allowing the mind to ramble has proven to be equally influential.[12] Only our Netflix addiction throws a spanner into the good works, for passive consumption – be that of substances or stream-ing content – can never really be truly restorative. On the bright side, though, binge-watching series may be prefer-able to washing copious amounts of mutton chops down with pints of milk while dying of boredom as we lie tied down to a bed.

S is for Stoicism

Over the past decade or so, there has been a notable renewal of interest, both in popular philosophy and in the literature of self-help, in the ancient philosophy known as Stoicism.[1] The reasons for this have a lot to do with the times in which we are now living, with their troubling similarities to the period when Stoicism first emerged. So, what's so great about Stoicism, and how can Stoic ideas help us grapple with our modern-day exhaustion?

Stoic philosophy first arose in ancient Greece around 300 BCE and flourished in the Greek and Roman worlds until the third century CE.[2] Stoics such as Seneca (c. 2 BCE–65 CE), Epictetus (c. 55–135 CE) and Marcus Aurelius (121–180 CE) believed that all suffering is in our minds. Our unhappiness, they argued, is caused not by external events but by our reactions to those events – more precisely, by a combination of faulty judgements and unrealistic expectations. The Stoics also held impressively pragmatic views about how we should spend our mental energies. Given that most external events are beyond our control, they believed that it is pointless to worry about them. Our evaluations of these events, by contrast, are completely within our control, for, ultimately, we are rational animals. Therefore, they recommend that we don't attach significance to *any* external phenomena or circumstance. Instead, all our mental energies should be directed to our inner life, with a view to controlling our thoughts.

The rich afterlife of Stoic thought is evident, for example, in Cognitive Behavioural Therapy (CBT), which seeks to teach us to control our emotions by controlling our thoughts, especially by challenging unproductive and irrational cognitions with rational counter-arguments. A modern Christian version of Stoic principles can also be found in Reinhold Niebuhr's serenity prayer. 'God grant me the serenity to accept the things I cannot change; courage to change the things I can; and wisdom to know the difference' has become a core mantra in twelve-step programmes such as Alcoholics Anonymous. Stoicism has had fans in the US military for decades, and many, mainly male, high-achieving entrepreneurs are currently keen on what has been dubbed Stoicism 2.0 – a more applicable, and perhaps less pessimistic, version of Stoicism mediated by self-help writers such as Ryan Holiday. The notion of psychological resilience is another offshoot of the Stoic tradition. Resilience is based on the idea that if we can't change our circumstances, we should instead concentrate on strengthening our inner resources so that we can cope more effectively with outer stressors.

The promise of sovereignty over our thoughts and emotions is of course extremely attractive. If we were truly able to control our minds, nothing could ever rattle us – no matter what terrible cards life might deal us. The prospect of control over our cognitive processes is even more appealing in times of uncertainty and rapid change. The more unstable our external circumstances, the more we long to establish steadiness within ourselves. It is no coincidence, then, that Stoicism should have flourished in times of great political instability. Most of the Stoics knew a thing or two about dramatic changes of fortune. Early in his career, the statesman Seneca was sentenced to death by the emperor Caligula. While the sentence was commuted, Seneca had to spend eight long and lonely years in exile in Corsica. Then he was recalled to Rome to teach the child who became the infamous emperor Nero, best known for having fiddled while Rome burned. Nero clearly ignored the teachings of his mentor: he became renowned for his cruelty, and eventually ordered his former teacher to commit suicide.

Before he became a philosopher, Epictetus was a disabled Greek slave, freed by a master who recognised his talent. During his reign, the emperor Marcus Aurelius had to contend with the flooding of the Tiber, famine and the plague, as well as various attempts to usurp him. We can see, then, why the Stoics were so concerned with how best to negotiate the fickleness of fortune. They saw empires rise and fall, great cities burn, ships sink and men of noble families be killed or enslaved. Moreover, the mood swings of absolute rulers could, quite literally, be deadly. Power, public office, money and reputation could be granted and withdrawn on a whim.

The Stoics accepted that there are many things we cannot control. All outer circumstances, they believed, are predetermined by fate. But rather than despairing at what they could not master, the Stoics decided to direct all of their mental energy to what they could: our responses to external events. Most of us would agree with their reasoning thus far. But the Stoics went further. Because we cannot control external phenomena, they argued that it follows that we should not attach significance to *any* such phenomena at all – that is, to anything that can be taken away from us. This would include not only our possessions, our reputation, food and drink, and the various pleasures of the flesh, but also our health, friends, partners, children – and even our lives.

'There is nothing either good or bad but thinking makes it so', writes Seneca.[3] And he adds: 'We are attracted by wealth, pleasures, good looks, political advancement and various other welcoming and enticing prospects: we are repelled by exertion, death, pain, disgrace and limited means. It follows that we need to train ourselves not to crave for the former and not to be afraid of the latter.'[4] To cope with the frailty of human existence, we must refuse to allow anything that goes badly for us to affect us emotionally. Only if we carry our valuables inside us – in the form of our beliefs and cognitive skills – can we become invincible, no matter what fortune hurls at us.

There are some obvious problems with this radical stance. First, the Stoics assume that we are always able to reason ourselves out of our own cognitive traps. But what if our reasoning itself has become muddied? What if our cognitive processes have become so distorted that we no longer recognise them as distorted? Would using our twisted reason then not be like trying to wash dishes in dirty dishwater? The Stoics also ignore another important source for changing our thoughts and emotions – our creative imagination. It is not only reason that can propel us out of bad mental states, but also art, stories, music and stunning landscapes, as well as smell, taste and touch. Perhaps most importantly, though, we are nothing like as rational as the ancient Stoics liked to think. We can't permanently exercise the kind of rigid rational control over our inner lives which the Stoics envisaged – for that, too, can become a deeply exhausting exercise and substantially drain our energy.[5]

It is also not wise to attempt not to care about matters of the heart. And nor are we quite as powerless regarding the control of external events as the Stoics believed. Although there are plenty of bad rulers in politics these days, we have usually voted them in, and few of them have the power to have us killed on a whim. There is, more generally speaking, no such clear-cut line between controllables and uncontrollables as the Stoics suggest. We can choose where to direct our attention, effort, commitment and care; we can adjust our consumption habits and try to live as healthily as possible; and we can seek relationships that are good for us. Our version of democracy also differs substantially from that of the Stoics – we can participate actively in communal and political life, and our actions in these spheres can have impact. Moreover, we grew up with concepts such as universal rights, so the passive acceptance of injustice and suffering feels less natural to us.

In reality, then, much of what matters to us is probably situated in a grey zone. Therefore, it is more helpful to assume that there are things we can control, things we can influence, and matters which we can't control, but about which we care. The zone of influence is the murky in-between, the liminal sphere that makes up much of life. Where we tend to set the boundaries between the different zones, moreover, has a lot to do with how we think about our agency, both individually and culturally. Optimists with a can-do attitude will feel they have a much broader sphere of control than pessimists, for example.[6] As various psychological experiments have demonstrated, Westerners generally tend to feel more in control of their environment than do Easterners.[7] It remains true, however, that our energies are finite. And certain events really are hard or nearly impossible to influence or change. Unfortunately, most of what other people think, do and feel falls into that category.

A powerful Stoic technique is the 'Circle of Control' exercise. It is particularly useful for the exhausted because it can help us make wiser decisions about where we may wish to focus our energies. By letting go of what we can't control, we can save a lot of energy that we can then direct elsewhere. And energy is of course in short supply when we are feeling depleted. So Stoic-style reflections on how to spend our energy are highly relevant. For this exercise, it is useful to accept the Stoic division of spheres of influence and assume that most external events are by definition beyond our control, while most internal events are within our control. External events include not just what other people do, feel or think, but also the climate and the weather, war, politics and economics, as well as our personal fortunes, health and the course of our careers. Internal events include our cognitive reactions to and emotional judgements of external events. For example, it is reasonable to assume that we cannot fully control whether we get a particular job or a promotion, whether people will like us, whether our product will sell, or whether someone we admire will accept our dinner invitation. But we can control how we respond when we aren't invited for an interview, when our promotion application is unsuccessful, when our product fails to sell, or when our dinner invitation is rebuffed.

To create your own 'Circle of Control', begin by compiling a list of your core stressors. Then draw three concentric circles nestling within each other on a piece of paper. The outer one is the zone of 'what I can't control'. The middle one is the 'sphere of influence'. And the innermost circle is 'what I can control'. Place your stressors in the relevant circles. Seneca and Co. would strongly advise you to ignore the outer two circles. They would recommend radical acceptance of these phenomena, and that you focus all your attention on managing your responses to them. This sounds much easier than it is, of course. For most of us, this would presumably constitute a truly radical transformation of our inland empires, and it also presupposes that we are able simply to let go of some of our greatest worries and bug-bears. Mind shifts of that magnitude never happen overnight, and often don't happen at all. Here too, our judgement and expectations are essential. Rather than hoping to master this task at first attempt, we may wish to think of it as a process – indeed, as a lifelong learning journey and a very gradual inner and outer reorientation. Our personal 'Circle of Control' can be a particularly useful guide when we feel most lacking in control.

Another key strategy for achieving the Stoic aim of absolute equanimity in the face of hardship is to regulate our desires. The Stoics recommend we align our desires with whatever is happening to us. In other words, they urge us to want what we have. But some of the external phenomena beyond our control are obviously preferable to others. It is clearly nicer to be wealthy, healthy, loved and sated with a roof over our head than the opposite. Seneca admitted that. He writes that he is not against our possessing these things. But he urges us to ensure that we possess them 'without tremors', by convincing ourselves that we can live happily without them, and 'by always regarding them as being on the point of vanishing'.[8] By contrast, Epictetus – the most hard-nosed of the Stoics – seems positively to welcome blows of fortune. Epictetus is firmly of the 'what doesn't kill you makes you stronger' school of thought. Life is suffering, bad things will happen. And when they do, we can use our bad luck to test our resolve. 'So when trouble comes', he argues, 'think of yourself as a wrestler whom God, like a trainer, has paired with a tough young buck. For what purpose? To turn you into Olympic-class material.'[9] Everything that fortune throws at me, Epictetus writes, 'I will transform into a blessing, a boon – something dignified, even enviable'.[10]

Marcus Aurelius' famous *Meditations* are perhaps the most beautiful and accessible of the ancient Stoic writings (Seneca's letters come a close second). The *Meditations* are not about mastery of the external world but, in true Stoic fashion, are purely about commanding the inner life. They are addressed to Aurelius himself, in the form of private reflections and reminders, and read like the (albeit highly sophisticated) journal of a Stoic trainee.[11] In this text, we find self-examinations, mental exercises and numerous maxims that beautifully capture Stoic thought. The *Meditations* detail the earnest efforts of someone who tries to put Stoic doctrine into practice in his everyday life and they illustrate just how much cognitive discipline being a Stoic requires.

Like Seneca and Epictetus before him, Aurelius sought above all to control his desires and judgements. We should only desire that which happens to us. Assuming any kind of agency over external events and wanting what we don't have are not just illogical but set us up for unnecessary failure. One of my favourite Aurelian maxims, which captures in a nutshell the importance of adjusting our expectations, is: 'Only a madman looks for figs in winter.'[12] There is so much wisdom in that image. If we want a friend who is caring and supportive, for example, we need to befriend someone who has the ability to act in this way. We shouldn't choose someone who tends to be preoccupied with their own dramas and has little or no capacity to listen or to give. If we know that our parents or partners are constitutionally incapable of expressing approval, we need to stop seeking it. There is no point in trying to impress the unimpressible, or trying to squeeze blood from a stone. In the same spirit, if we want our website built or our portrait painted, we need to go to someone who can actually code or paint. We often have expectations of people which they simply cannot fulfil. The Stoics argue that it is always our unrealistic expectations which do us harm, not the actions of others. Aurelius advises that 'Harm to you cannot subsist in another's directing mind, nor indeed in any turn or change of circumstance. Where, then? In that part of you which judges harm. So no such judgment, and all is well.'[13] In other words, it is we alone who can make ourselves hurt. We are the sole producers of our inner pain. This is an insight that is both frightening and liberating.

The Stoics have no time for feelings of bitterness about the cards we may have been dealt by fate, rejecting the very notion of victimhood. Our culture of *ressentiment* would be completely alien to them. Everyone suffers bad fortune, that is simply the way things are. The sooner we accept that fact, the better. The Stoics expect life to be suffering. Our own horizon of expectation in the West today, by contrast, couldn't be more different. We tend to expect not just happiness and well-being but also a largely trouble-free life. Many of us feel a strong sense of injustice when that life is not granted to us.

Finally, the Stoics understood that self-improvement requires hard and constant effort. As Aurelius knew well, becoming a Stoic is a lifetime's pursuit and requires absolute commitment to the cause. This is also an optimistic thought, though, for the Stoics believed in lifelong learning and continuous improvement. We can all train our minds, and our minds can continue to learn and change. Recent research on neuroplasticity confirms the Stoics' faith in our ability to change our thought-patterns.[14] And yet, while our brains are plastic, it is important to note that they are not 'not made of PlayDoh', as the psychologist John

Sharp reminds us. 'Forging new neurological connections doesn't happen overnight. You have to live as a new person before you can become a new person.'[15] What is more, unlike many of us today, the Stoics did not embark on this quest to avoid pain and displeasure. An increase in their happiness levels was not their aim. Instead, they simply sought to cultivate a mental attitude that meets whatever fate throws at us with composure and resilience.

T is for Time

Lost time – what is this elusive phenomenon, pursued so determinedly by Marcel Proust in his great multi-volume novel *In Search of Lost Time*? A haunting, tyrannical force, the idea of lost time plays a key role in our collective exhaustion. In the past, injunctions such as *carpe diem* (seize the day) and *memento mori* addressed archetypal anxieties about human finitude. These remain active today, but are now complemented by our own particular time-related fears, which revolve predominantly around productivity and wasted potential.

Most of us have internalised deeply damaging attitudes towards time. They are evident in the everyday metaphors we use to talk about it. We think of time as something that doesn't merely pass but that can be both quantified and commodified. Time is something we can waste, kill, lose, master, spend, save, budget for and buy. Time has become money, as Benjamin Franklin famously put it. Since the advent of the Industrial Revolution, we have begun to think of time as a precious commodity that can be used sensibly or foolishly. Moreover, whether or not we use our limited time on earth wisely has become a moral question.[1] Wasting time, as the Puritans held, is a mortal sin.

The definition of time wisely spent usually entails activities that are future-orientated and that require the delay of gratification and impulse control. Work is chief amongst these. Wise expenditure of time is manifest in not giving in to the siren call of the pleasure principle, or our desire to rest, laze and slack, and to take a more grown-up, long-term view.

During the Victorian age, punctuality was deemed to be among the core virtues. Bad time management and, relatedly, deficient self-discipline skills were seen as one of the major moral failings of the poor.[2] Today, we may still be chastised for wasting our employer's time by being late, missing deadlines, working inefficiently or too slowly, or by procrastinating or idling. Yet most of us probably live in fear of a much graver, existential form of time-wasting: wasting our lives by failing to realise ourselves, not living up to our potential, not finding our calling or true love, or else neglecting to spend enough time with our loved ones and on our relationships.

What do you consider time wasted, time lost and time well spent – and why? How much of your day do you expend killing time, wishing you could fast-forward to some point in the future – the weekend, or the next holiday? For whom, or what, do you have a lot of time? Do you live by the dictates of clock time, or are you attuned to more ancient forms of temporal measurement – the circadian rhythm, the lunar calendar, the movement of the tides, the passing of the seasons or sidereal time, the absolute time of the heavens?

Some of us live in the present, with most of our attention focused on the here and now. Others find that our thoughts are constantly being pulled to the past or rushing ahead to the future, planning and rehearsing our next activities. Some of us are nostalgic pessimists, pining for a long-lost golden age, while others subscribe to the Hegelian notion of progress – believing that humanity is marching onwards and upwards to an ever-brighter future. Some imagine time as linear or circular in nature, others think of it as a marvellously looping thing with portals and knots that follows laws far too complex for the limited human mind.

Our attitudes to time can be very revealing of deeper values and cultural beliefs. The historian E. P. Thompson has explored how technological advances ushered in a moral change, 'a new Puritan discipline and bourgeois exactitude'.[3] He was particularly interested in the effect of the spread of church towers with bells ringing out the hours in the fourteenth century, and pendulum clocks in households as well as portable time in the form of pocket watches in the seventeenth century. Industry and time-discipline became the external markers of a person's value, not just in a religious but also in a labour-market sense. Thompson writes: 'By the 1830s and 1840s it was commonly observed that the English industrial worker was marked off from his fellow Irish worker, not by a greater capacity for hard work, but by his regularity, his methodical paying-out of energy, and perhaps also by a repression, not of enjoyments, but of the capacity to relax in the old, uninhibited ways.'[4] 'Without time-discipline', he concludes, 'we could not have the insistent energies of industrial man.'[5]

Pre-industrial peoples measured time by tasks – familiar, everyday processes, such as the time it takes to boil rice, to go to market, to roast a chicken, to fry a locust or to say an Ave Maria. The more complex our labour processes became, the more clock-time rose in importance. With the division of labour, the need to synchronise it became imperative. Think production lines and factory work, and how calamitous being out of synch was for the character played by Charlie Chaplin in *Modern Times* (1936). It is not surprising, then, that arguments in favour of time-thriftiness first peaked in the nineteenth century – the age of industry, social mobility and industrial capitalism. These attitudes have remained with us. Indeed, we have collectively internalised the notion of lost time as a moral issue, and become our own strict supervisors.

My own attitudes to time reflect this more general cultural turn. And they are quite sad. For as long as I can remember, I have felt that I should always be working – that any time not spent on my projects is wasted. Because I inevitably fall short of this ego-ideal of perma-work, I feel guilty a lot. I find it hard to relax. I find it almost impossible to contemplate a fifteen-minute walk in the sunshine in my lunch break – which, naturally, is as short as can be, and often spent in front of my computer. I rarely meet friends for lunch or during the day, although whenever I do it makes me happy.

Most paradoxically, it is on the days when I have an abundance of uninterrupted time to work on my projects, with no other obligations and commitments, that I tend to waste my time most egregiously. The more of it I have, the less wisely I use it. Every couple of minutes I refresh the *Guardian* homepage to check the newest doomsday headlines. Like a mindless chicken looking for digital corn, I click on my email to see what has come in. I answer most emails immediately because I fear an unmanageable build-up in my inbox – falling behind on tasks, loss of control, chaos. I scroll pointlessly through Twitter feeds that leave me feeling despondent and exhausted. All of these displacement activities probably amount to two or three hours of lost time a day.

I know all this at a rational level, and still it is inconceivable for me to allow myself to read a book for pleasure, to chat to a friend on the phone, to take a nap or to do nothing at all. I feel like I just have to sit in front of my laptop, even if my mind is elsewhere and nothing manifests on the page. I am shockingly stingy with my time when it comes to seeing others, limiting coffees and drinks and other engagements to shortish time slots. I have to force myself, every single time, to go to social gatherings, in spite of the fact that, when I'm there, I'm almost always glad that I went. But my instinct is to protect my working time at all costs. What saves me from myself is that I make a major exception for my hobbies, to all of which I am very happy to devote time, simply because they make me happy.

None of this is remotely reasonable. Even from a productivity point of view, it makes no sense. I know very well that if I took regular breaks, went to work in cafes, had lunch with people who make me laugh, and did joyful energy-restoring things between working slots, I'd be a much better and more prolific writer. In addition to not being conducive to productivity, my twisted temporal sensibilities are quite obviously a recipe for a fairly miserable and isolated existence. Of course this kind of behaviour is also exhausting. It is precisely in this guilt-infested grey zone where the danger of burnout resides – when we languish, trapped in a state in which we can neither work well nor allow ourselves properly to rest or play. We are most at risk of burning out when we become prisoners of our own injurious work ethic, when we are unable to climb out of these cages of our own making.

And I know I'm far from being alone in this – many friends and coaching clients report very similar harmful work and time habits. Most of us remain immune to sensible calls to devote more time to recreational activities and our relationships. Why is that the case? Why are we all so trapped? Perhaps we are wary of the instrumental logic of this kind of advice – for ultimately, self-care and recreation time, too, are designed to enhance our productivity, in other words, to make us better people and to stop us from wasting time.

Our fear of lost time is clearly a wider cultural malaise. It is no doubt anchored in a paradoxical Puritan inheritance, paired up with pragmatic capitalist necessity. Our thinking is shaped by economics – everything is assessed in terms of gain and loss, with productivity and efficiency our existential yardsticks. But there is also our growing inability to stop doing and simply to *be*. We are driven by an urge to be relentlessly active, always to be project- and future-focused. For what might we find if we stopped? What would surface? It's a catch-22 situation: the more of our time we dedicate to work, the emptier our life becomes in other domains, and the more scary it is to stop working and to confront that emptiness.

What can we do about all of this? We may be neither able nor willing to become full-blown contemplatives, or to join the tribe of other time rebels – beatniks, bohemians, hippies, punks, slackers and dropouts, who are united by their rejection of conventional time values. But there is no doubt that our crude commodified conception of time demands far too high a psychological toll. We must, therefore, take the question for whom or what we wish to make time in our lives extremely seriously. It should be a question we ask ourselves every day.

We may also wish to look far more critically at the notion of lost time. Although it takes Proust's narrator, Marcel, many years before he finally finds his calling and becomes a novelist, not a single minute of these years was actually lost. Quite the contrary, because every single experience, perception, thought, feeling, interaction and relationship, and every seemingly squandered year, contributed to making him the writer he became. All was learning. Nothing was wasted at all.

It is, then, both an individual and a broader cultural challenge for us to rediscover 'the joy that dwells far within slow time', as poet John O'Donohue put it. In his blessing for the exhausted, he recommends:

You have travelled too fast over false ground;
Now your soul has come, to take you back.

Take refuge in your senses, open up
To all the small miracles you rushed through.

Exhausted

Become inclined to watch the way of rain
When it falls slow and free.

Imitate the habit of twilight,
Taking time to open the well of colour
That fostered the brightness of day.

Draw alongside the silence of stone
Until its calmness can claim you.

Be excessively gentle with yourself.[6]

U is for Urgency

Most of us are neither currency traders, nor emergency room surgeons, nor firefighters. So why do we feel a sense of constant urgency when it comes to work and to life more generally? Why do we believe that everything will fall apart if we take our eyes off our screens for just five minutes? We tend to act as though dealing with our tasks as swiftly as possible is a matter of life and death. And while it may often feel that way, it is, statistically speaking, almost never the case. Urgency has become part of our culture, and yet it is very rarely a response to actual emergencies. One of the genuine emergencies that we should be addressing collectively is climate change – and yet on that matter we have managed to procrastinate for almost fifty years. A few hundred years ago, it could take weeks or months for a letter to reach its addressee. Today, our communications are instantaneous. And for that very reason, we have also come to expect immediate responses to our requests, in both our private and our working lives. Inboxes overflowing with emails that call for actions not yet taken have become a new kind of accusatory to-do list. A sign of our not being able to keep up with the pace of modern life, the full inbox is the new emblem of our lack of control.

Technological innovation in communications has a lot to do with the more general sense of urgency that shapes our lives. The sociologist Hartmut Rosa argues that the history of modernity is the history of acceleration. That acceleration is particularly acutely felt in the domains of transportation, trade and communication. Not all of it is bad, of course. But the speed of social, economic and technological change has now taken on a life of its own, and Rosa believes that we can no longer really keep up. This has a highly detrimental impact on our quality of life. In the pre-modern era, social change was 'intergenerational', which means that social structures changed very slowly, over the course of multiple generations. With a few exceptions, people didn't really notice the effects of such change. Today, we have to adapt more or less constantly within each generation to significant changes to our everyday lives. Most of these changes are technology-related, and have dramatically transformed how we travel, do business and relate to one another. The Silent Generation, Boomers and Gen Xers had to learn how to board planes, use hoovers, microwaves, computers, mobile phones, WhatsApp and Zoom, as well as how to shop and to bank online. Although digital natives, Millennials and Gen Zers have had to contend with major cultural, economic and political shifts, many of them negative. Saddled with student debt, they have grown up under the shadow of climate collapse, populism and the culture wars, and find themselves struggling in precarious job and unaffordable housing markets.

Unlike previous generations, we are now likely to have to change our professions more than once, and if we don't constantly upskill and upgrade, our expertise can become obsolete very quickly. I'm no technophobe, and not yet that old, but at the beginning of each academic year I spent a few panicky days trying to figure out how to use constantly changing software for lecture recording, marking, student quizzes, feedback sessions and sharing course materials. I worried that one day I wouldn't manage and would officially become a dinosaur, stumbling into the lecture theatre clutching nothing but an armful of handwritten notes on yellowing paper, unable even to switch on the hyper-complex lighting system. I don't know how to show clips, set up Calendly, drop a pin or order an Uber. The few apps I have on my phone were downloaded for me by eye-rolling younger people. My smart TV is definitely much smarter than I am.

Technological progress was supposed to result in our gaining time, because most machines and inventions were designed to do time-consuming labour for us, and more quickly and efficiently than we could ever dream. Think trains, cars and planes, but also production lines, washing machines, dishwashers, email and search engines. Hartmut Rosa argues that what happened instead was that we had to learn to keep up with the speed of all these innovations. While emails are clearly faster and easier to send than telegrams, letters and memos, their volume has increased to such an extent that managing incoming messages now takes up a considerable proportion of our working day. While cars can get us from A to B far more quickly than a horse, we now spend more time commuting to ever more remote workplaces. While vacuum cleaners and washing machines originally saved quite significant amounts of time, we also saw a rapid rise in standards of cleanliness to which we had to adhere, in tandem with what the new appliances could deliver. And while we no longer have to go to libraries and archives to hunt for information, the amount of accessible digital information has exploded to such an extent that selecting, processing and digesting what is relevant and accurate has become a Sisyphean challenge in its own right. We have, then, become a high-speed society – with wide-ranging ethical and psychological consequences. Rosa believes that we are at a point of 'frenetic standstill' – everything is constantly moving, often at a dizzying pace, while most deeper structures and privileges remain unchanged.[1]

And yet, laments about acceleration are not new. In *The Communist Manifesto* (1848), Marx and Engels bemoaned the fact that 'all fixed, fast-frozen relations' were being swept away, that 'all new-formed ones' were becoming 'antiquated before they can ossify', and that 'all that is solid melts into air'.[2] In 1882, in *The Gay Science*, the German philosopher Friedrich Nietzsche also complained about the growing sense of urgency. He blamed the Americans. Their love of money, he wrote,

and the breathless haste with which they work – the distinctive vice of the new world – is already beginning to infect old Europe with its ferocity and is spreading a lack of spirituality like a blanket. Even now one is ashamed of resting, and prolonged reflection almost gives people a bad conscience. One thinks with a watch in one's hand, even as one eats one's midday meal while reading the latest news of the stock market; one lives as if one always 'might miss out on something.' ... Living in a constant chase after gain compels people to expend their spirit to the point of exhaustion in continual pretense and overreaching and anticipating others. Virtue has come to consist of doing something in less time than someone else.[3]

Nietzsche was describing early versions of burnout culture, FOMO, the spiritual pitfalls of materialism and a new fetishisation of speed as a value in its own right. Many French and German physicians and psychiatrists, too, complained about the hustle and bustle of nineteenth-century urban life, the relentless chasing of entertainment, money and inappropriate objects of desire, and constant information overload. They deemed these phenomena to be serious threats to the delicate nervous systems of sensitive brainworkers, as well as to hard-working captains of industry. Human beings, they claimed, were not suited to resist the onslaught of all these urban stimuli. They concluded that the permanent state of urgency in modern life had become a serious threat to people's mental and physical health.[4]

The German writer Heinrich Mann (brother of the better-known Thomas Mann) captured the spirit of this injurious urgency in his novella *Dr Bieber's Temptation* (1898). In this story, Herr Sägemüller complains about the 'brutality and coarseness of reality' that now 'assaults us both at home and outdoors'. He goes on to assert that the electrical tram 'intervenes as insolently into my life as the phone wires that are whirring outside my bedroom window at night. Advertisements on the street corners and the howling of the trade people and the press, bells ringing everywhere, bikes and motorcars – all of these phenomena rape my senses; I am entirely defenseless.'[5]

And then there is the breathless jeremiad of the German psychiatrist Wilhelm Erb, writing in 1884. Erb was concerned about the fact that all affairs are conducted in 'haste and excitement' which chronically overstrains our nervous systems. He blamed this transformation on an 'excessive increase in traffic and the wire-networks of our telegraphs and telephones', as well as new global trading patterns. In addition, he observed that

> the worrying repercussions of serious political, industrial, and financial crises permeate into much wider circles of the population than in the past; the general public now participates in public life; political, religious, and social battles, party politics, election campaigns, and the excessive dominance of clubs and societies overheat people's heads and force their spirits to undertake ever new exertions while robbing them of the time for rest, sleep, and stillness.

He concludes that 'life in big cities has become ever more refined and restless'.[6]

The negative impact of a sense of urgency is far from limited to modernity, however, as is demonstrated by my favourite example, from *The Yellow Emperor's Classic of Medicine*. This work is one of the most important written sources of Daoism, and has been attributed to Huang Di, the Yellow Emperor, who reigned during the middle of the third millennium BCE. In it, a character called Qi Bo complains:

> In the past, people practiced the Tao, the Way of Life. They understood the principle of balance, of yin and yang ... They ate a balanced diet at regular times, arose and retired at regular hours, avoided overstressing their bodies and minds, and refrained from overindulgence of all kinds. They maintained well-being of body and mind; thus, it is not surprising that they lived over one hundred years. These days, people have changed their way of life. They drink wine as though it were water, indulge excessively in destructive activities, drain their jing – the body's essence that is stored in the kidneys – and deplete their qi. They do not know the secret of conserving their energy and vitality. Seeking emotional excitement and momentary pleasures, people disregard the natural rhythm and order of the universe. They fail to regulate their lifestyle and diet, and sleep improperly. So it is not surprising that they look old at fifty and die soon after.[7]

Over 4,000 years ago, then, elders were already appalled by the ways in which younger generations lived their lives, upsetting the slower, natural rhythms of the universe. They castigated their undue urgency and the reckless squandering of their energies by chasing fleeting pleasures. There is, for sure, also a generational dimension to the perception of unwarranted urgency. On the one hand, the fact that we are not alone in feeling the pressures of acceleration is soothing. And yet it is also concerning. For if our forebears were already concerned about the impact of telegrams and trains on their delicate nervous systems, what hope is there for us, living as we do in a world of constant change?

There are other ways in which we can look at our struggles with urgency. The Silicon Valley psychotherapist Stephanie Brown, for example, proposes that her clients' 'pulsing sense of urgency is a form of self-medication – something they were doing as a way not to feel something else'. Their various forms of 'high-speed living' are, she says, 'serving as some kind of emotional avoidance'. She likens her permanently stressed, compulsively hurried clients with their 'addiction to speed' to alcoholics, arguing that their chronic sense of urgency is a strategy to control their emotions. Like all behaviours to which we can become addicted, an addiction to urgency has secondary gains. It is usually accompanied by a feeling of exhilaration, 'an intoxicating thrill to living at warp speed'.[8]

Moreover, as Oliver Burkeman points out, addiction to urgency is also a socially sanctioned, if not celebrated, compulsion: urgency addicts are usually perceived as driven, highly conscientious people who are in constant demand. And yet, as one of the people I coach told me, this may well change, for the ultimate status symbol now is slow time. He said that while the rich compete with each other through conspicuous consumption of expensive Rolex watches, the ultra-rich don't wear watches at all, because they are masters of their own time, on call to no one.

Urgency is also related to our inability to be present, to concentrate on the here and now, and to accept the natural rhythm of things. Many of us live mentally in the future, endlessly trying to get through our to-do lists, in what Marilynne Robinson describes as a state of 'joyless urgency'. But urgency is more than just a panicked reaction to acceleration, an exhilarating addiction to speed and a failure to live in the moment. It is also a form of impatience – both collective and individual in nature. Franz Kafka considered impatience to be our original sin, the reason for Eve and Adam's eviction from the Garden of Eden: 'Because of impatience they were expelled; because of impatience they do not return', he wrote.[9] Because we are so used to speed and to seamless efficiency, every minor delay, every rupture in the smooth functioning of things, presents itself to us as an injustice, robbing us of precious time.

Many of us today are unable to tolerate any kind of delay with dignified equanimity. We swear in call queues and exasperatedly honk our horns one second after the lights have turned green. Traffic jams, people who don't immediately respond to our messages, an Amazon delivery that takes twenty-five rather than twenty-four hours, a cash machine that disposes bank notes with a five-second delay, slow Wi-Fi and supermarket queues have the power to discombobulate and enrage.[10] The ancient theologians were right in understanding impatience as a minor cousin of wrath.

But whither do we hasten so fervently? Why do we rush through wonderland like the white rabbit, clutching our watches, unable to slow down and enjoy all the strange and beautiful creatures and sights that we encounter? What great prize awaits us when we have urged and pressed enough, completed all our tasks at maximum speed, and met our deadlines well in advance? What, exactly, is urgency's endgame?

V is for Vampires

The explanations of what drains our energies vary considerably across the ages, and also across cultures. Humans have seen their exhaustion as being caused by both internal and external forces, by imbalances in our humoral economy and by a faster pace of life, by inner psychological battles and by brain work, by weak faith and by the movements of the planets. It has also been blamed on diet, overexcitement and constant sensual overstimulation. Nowadays we tend to hold unmanageable workloads, toxic working environments and our permanent connectedness via electronic devices responsible for our collective weariness. But what about other people? How might those around us contribute to making us feel so depleted?

It is not a coincidence that the figure of the vampire has remained a highly attractive trope through the centuries. The core characteristic of vampires is that they drain the life energy from other beings in the form of their blood. Trapped in a liminal zone between life and death, vampires cannot sustain themselves, and either deplete, kill or turn their victims into their own kind in their unceasing quest for sustenance. However, they tend not to take what they need by force, but instead seduce their prey – according to legend, they have to be invited in. Many are simultaneously seductive and repulsive, and grand masters in the art of deception and manipulation. They lack a soul and therefore also a reflection in the mirror, are allergic to sunlight, silver and garlic, and can shape-shift into bats and other animals. In literature and film, vampires have served as projection planes for various forms of otherness: they tend to represent the dark and repressed aspects of our sexuality, or else fears of foreigners or exploitation. They can also signify addiction and greed, for their appetite is boundless.

While there are many reasons for our enduring fascination with these creatures of the night, one of those reasons is related to deeper anxieties about the secret depletion of our energy by other people. In vampire lore, blood signifies life, health, youth and above all energy. Femmes fatales, too, are associated with sucking the life force (in their case, sexual in nature) from their unsuspecting male victims. Other beings associated with energy depletion are succubae. All of these creatures gradually weaken and exhaust their prey, who waste away and often die unless the cause of their loss of energy is discovered and eliminated.

Who might be the energy vampires in our own lives? Ideally, relationships are based on a mutual cycle of giving and taking, where both parties contribute an equal amount of care and attention to the other. In times of trouble, when our loved ones are temporarily helpless and vulnerable, the dynamic changes, of course. But the expectation is that, if it were the other way round, they would also be there to support us in the same way. There are some relationships in which the energy exchange is not equal, and where our role is that of the giver: this is true when we care for young children, elderly parents or other vulnerable people whom we love. In these cases, our charges are not the vampires – instead, it is the act of caring itself that can be extremely depleting. As an altruistic act of love, giving care of that kind can be extremely satisfying, but it can also be a great challenge, especially if we have to provide intensive physical or emotionally demanding care over a period of many years. Many long-term carers find it increasingly hard to care for themselves as well as their loved ones, and are often plagued by guilt and shame whenever they try to meet their own needs. Carer syndrome is a very real and dangerous form of burnout.

One of the most common relationship problems is when the amount of energy we give is permanently out of kilter, but without this being openly agreed or acknowledged. When we give and give without getting enough back, our relationships may turn into energy-depleting experiences that can be very damaging for our mental health. They can take the form of partnerships in which one partner does all the running, planning and emotional labour, or in which someone does all the chores. We all know that the unfair distribution of tasks – be they manual, attentional or the labours of love – can become serious sources of discontent. That is as true for communities as it is for relationships. Sadly, there is often a significant gender gap when it comes to childcare, household chores and the emotional labour that is involved in planning our and our children's social lives. The sociologist Arlie Russell Hochschild has coined the term 'The Second Shift' to describe the double burden of working mothers who also perform most domestic tasks as well as their paid labour, and who, understandably, struggle with these demands on their time and energy.[1]

Even more extreme scenarios of lopsided energy exchanges involve people who knowingly use and exploit others, often in ways that drain one's social battery or are otherwise exhausting and unrewarding to deal with. In recent years, there has been a striking increase in interest in narcissists and their uniquely manipulative ways. Narcissists loom large in the popular imagination. The internet is awash with articles such as 'A Field Guide to Spotting Narcissists', 'Is my Partner a Narcissist?' and 'Navigating Narcissism at Work'. It seems that many people feel they have at least one narcissist in their lives, and seek to find out how to protect themselves from their exploits.

Narcissism is a spectrum and can range from a mild tendency to a clinical disorder: Narcissistic Personality Disorder (NPD). Narcissists desperately need other people to validate their own worth – admiration and attention are their vampiric currency. Like vampires, narcissists can be seductive. Often charismatic, charming, confident, witty, eloquent and superficially popular, they project a sense of invincibility and highly positive self-regard. However, their confidence is only skin-deep. At some point, their self-absorption becomes obvious for all to see. They also tend to live tumultuous lives, because when people eventually see through them, they usually cut ties. Narcissists are lacking in empathy and compassion, treat others as objects and often thrive as salesmen or entrepreneurs. Completely immune to self-doubt, they are easily offended and tend to harbour deep grudges. While the neurotic generally thinks it is their fault when things go wrong, often taking responsibility for matters that are clearly beyond their control, clinical narcissists always blame others and refuse to take any responsibility for their own failings. In their book, it is always the world that is at fault.

Yet, like vampires, narcissists have a significant weakness: they simply cannot exist without a constant supply of external validation. It's their life blood. And we have the power to withhold that validation from them. In an ideal world, we would be able to avoid narcissists once we have identified them. Cutting them out of our lives is undoubtedly the best strategy, for, sadly, attempts to reform or cure narcissists are almost always doomed to fail. The clinical literature is clear on this point: the chances of people who suffer from narcissistic personality disorder changing their ways are extremely slim.[2] They have built a shell around their very fragile ego, protecting it from reality, and they will defend this construct at all costs. For when that narcissistic shell cracks, the narcissist's world falls apart and they are at a very high risk of suicide. They rarely let that happen, though, and equally rarely seek therapy, because they cannot admit to themselves that there might be something wrong with them. Instead, they blame others when things don't go their way.

Sometimes, however, we cannot simply cut narcissists out of our lives. They may be our partners, family members, bosses or co-workers. If we have to maintain contact with a narcissist, we need to develop ways of defending ourselves. Above all, it is essential to distinguish what is and what is not within our control. First, while we cannot change the narcissist's behaviour, we can manage our expectations. By expecting little or nothing from them, we render them unable to disappoint or disconcert us. Remember Marcus Aurelius' remark that 'Only a madman looks for figs in winter' (see 'S is for Stoicism')? A clear-eyed Stoic approach will serve us well when we find ourselves having to engage with a narcissist. We should accept that they will not change, and adjust our expectations and actions accordingly. We also need to learn how to resist being lured back in after they have hurt us, and seek not to be seduced by the little they give, for they always give strategically.

Secondly, in some situations it can be useful superficially to supply the narcissist with what they most crave. For we, too, can use flattery and give attention in a more calculated manner if we must. By understanding what narcissists need most and what they fear, we can be as manipulative as they are. That is far from an ideal option, however, for it sullies us in the exchange. It should be used only when we have no alternative.

Thirdly, we can deliberately withdraw what narcissists crave so that they are forced to look for it elsewhere and eventually leave us alone. The best technique for depriving a narcissist of their sustenance is 'grey rocking'. When we find ourselves in an exchange with a narcissist, psychologists suggest imagining that we are a grey rock, impenetrable and indifferent to the waves that are lashing us. We should seek to be as uninterested and as uninteresting as possible. In other words, when we engage in conversations with a narcissist, we should be excessively boring. In that way, we deliberately starve narcissists of the attention and engagement on which they thrive. We also withhold information about ourselves that they might later use to draw us in. As the therapist Holly Richmond puts it: 'You're this immovable, impenetrable force who is disinterested. If they ask you a question, say yes or no, and don't give details about your life.'[3] We can also offer them a vacuous 'aha', 'wow', 'interesting' or 'wicked', ideally in a completely flat tone of voice. No more than that. We should, finally, also seek to avoid eye contact and not betray any kind of emotional response to what they are saying. Initially, this will greatly annoy, even enrage, the narcissist, and they may try even harder to provoke a reaction in us. In the long run, however, they are likely to leave us in peace, seeing us as someone who has nothing to offer them. Their neediness will take them elsewhere.

Fourthly, we should try not to harm or hate the narcissist. Setting firm boundaries and developing workable strategies of self-defence is not the same thing as seeking to cause harm. Self-defence is always ethically legitimate, while attack, even counter-attack, is often not. It is important not to sink to the narcissist's level. The techniques outlined above are reasonable and pragmatic moves designed to protect ourselves from future harm. Yet hating the narcissist, or plotting revenge, would also be a waste of our energy. And paradoxically, by hating them we would still be giving them what they crave – our attention and a strong emotional reaction. The most devastating thing we can do to a narcissist is to ignore them and to thrive despite them. As the Buddha said: 'Holding on to anger is like

drinking poison and expecting the other person to die.'
It is also worth remembering that narcissists are as much
slaves to their conditions as are vampires. They are generally not happy people. Forever trapped in their own fragile
fantasies of grandiosity, they have no true self-knowledge
and therefore no ability ever to develop. They can't form
lasting and deep relationships and are incapable of genuine
intimacy. In other words, although they might be highly
successful people in career terms, their lives looking shiny
and glamorous from the outside, they have their own cross
to bear.

We also need to remember that narcissism is not just an
individual problem. The perceived increase of energy-suck-
ing narcissists in our lives is at least partly a consequence
of a wider cultural shift. Narcissism is a condition frequently associated with selfie-snapping millennials and
Generation Y, with shamelessly self-promoting influencers
and with the disgraced 45th president of the United States.
The latter has normalised what was only a few years ago
considered self-aggrandising behaviour that was simply
beyond the pale. However, these are merely symptoms of
broader social changes.

Psychologists such as Jean Twenge have argued that
there has been a measurable increase in narcissism in
younger generations, which manifests in feelings of grandiosity, need for admiration and lack of empathy.[4] Twenge
traced this surge in narcissistic traits in younger people
back to the self-esteem movement, as well as a more general
fetishisation of self-worth in the West. Another factor
might be having to carve out spaces in a hyper-competitive

techno-capitalist society in which uniqueness and difference, as well as self-realisation and the ability to sell, are highly valorised qualities.

A growing number of psychologists now view our focus on self-esteem very critically. They relate it not only to a steep increase in narcissism and entitlement-thinking but also to low resilience in coping with failure and a growing lack of pro-social behaviours. The psychologist Roy Baumeister, who has analysed a large number of studies on self-esteem, takes a particularly dim view of the concept. 'After all these years', he writes, 'I'm sorry to say, my recommendation is this: forget about self-esteem and concentrate more on self-control and self-discipline.'[5]

While he is probably not wrong, we may find his advice a tad too Victorian. We would do better simply to shift our attention from self-esteem to self-acceptance. We may also wish to extend this acceptance to the vampires in our lives. They are who they are, shaped by their DNA, parenting and wider cultural forces. And while we should not seek to excuse their behaviour, nor let them suck our own life energy, we should try to accept that they and their kind will in all likelihood continue to populate the earth, just like their undead literary antecedents.

W is for Work

The idea that we realise ourselves through our work is a distinctly modern phenomenon. Today, work is central both to our personal lives and to our collective imagination. When we meet someone for the first time, our first question is likely to be: What do you do? Meaning, who are you? Both as individuals and as a society, we massively overinvest in work. Work has long ceased to be merely a means to earn a living and to secure social status. It has become deeply entangled with our other core needs. Those needs include meaning, identity, connection and self-realisation. And this entanglement is precisely where the problem lies. Many of us expect our work to furnish us with existential validation, to provide us with purpose and to help us realise our true potential – whatever that may be.

But while our expectations of work have skyrocketed, the reality of work is in many cases disappointing or dire. This growing gap between ideal and reality is a recipe for widespread suffering. As Jonathan Malesic observes, we often burn out because we simply expect too much of work. Work has become dangerously overdetermined.[1] Work is a cruel mistress from whom we expect nothing less than salvation. But in most cases, she does little but inflict pain. The social pain we experience when we feel isolated or mistreated at work can be as extreme as physical pain. It activates the same regions in our brains.[2] When things go wrong at work, we are affected at a psychological, social and spiritual level. In other words, work woes can impact profoundly upon our entire being.

When were we sold the idea that work, self-realisation and purpose should go hand in hand? Is it yet another neo-liberal coup designed to make us more engaged and productive? A brilliant strategy for enhancing our compliancy, to nip any revolutionary energies in the bud, and to turn us into our own harsh impresarios? Or are these expectations in fact indicative of educated middle-class privilege and an arrogant sense of self-entitlement? Perhaps our need for our work to be intrinsically meaningful is in the same category as our desire for avocado toast, *poke* bowls and goat yoga?

There is no doubt that work matters, if only in a quantitative way. On average, we spend c. 85,000 hours, or 3,500 full days, of our lives working.[3] Even when we are not physically at work, it can continue to absorb our energies and to colonise our thoughts. We may think of work simply as paid employment, the business of exchanging our time and skills for money, but there are also many non-remunerated forms of work, such as housework, childcare or emotional labour. At the most extreme end of the spectrum, those exploited under modern slavery are trapped in endless unremunerated work, often to pay off impossibly large 'debts' claimed by their captors.[4]

Work was long thought of as a purely physical activity. In ancient times and during the Middle Ages, physical work was primarily the domain of slaves, women, children and serfs. The concept of mental work began to come to the fore around the twelfth century, when scholars started to write about their intellectual fatigue. Before them, monks such as Evagrius Ponticus and John Cassian had already written about the tiring challenges of spiritual work. Nowadays, we tend to use the concept increasingly liberally. Everything is work: we speak of having to 'work' on our relationships, our effectiveness and our health and fitness – for example by 'working out' in the gym. Personal development is 'inner work', and even Freud talked about 'dream-work' and 'working things through'.

There are two main ancient positions on work, and they are diametrically opposed.[5] One camp thinks of work as God's curse on humanity – his punishment for apple-gate, Eve and Adam's primal act of disobedience. In this conception of work, it is aligned with sweat and the painful, often thankless toiling of an unyielding, thorn- and thistle-covered earth. Work is in the same punishing category as patriarchy, childbirth, death and returning into dust. In Genesis, God tells Adam:

Because thou hast hearkened unto the voice of thy wife, and hast eaten of the tree, of which I commanded thee, saying, Thou shalt not eat of it: cursed *is* the ground for thy sake; in sorrow shalt though eat *of* it all the days of thy life;

Thorns also and thistles shall it bring forth to thee, and thou shalt eat the herb of the field;

In the sweat of thy face shalt thou eat bread, till thou

return unto the ground; for out of it wast thou taken:
for dust thou *art*, and unto dust shalt thou return.[6]

God clearly associates work with strenuous effort,
exhaustion and endless suffering. The underlying assump-
tion here is that human beings are naturally idle and that
we all dream of returning to some version of Eden or the
Land of Cockaigne, in which milk and honey flow, and
fruit, roasted birds and wine bottles land in our laps while
we are relaxing in the shade. Following in this tradition,
the Benedictines and other Christian orders also saw work
as penitence, a mortification of the flesh and the spirit,
and an opportunity for atonement. It is worth noting that
the French verb *travailler*, 'to toil, labour', comes from the
Latin *trepalium*, an instrument of torture.[7]

The ancient defenders of work, by contrast, naturally
saw the matter differently. They pointed out that God
himself was working during the creation of the world. The
scholar Keith Thomas observes that work was also seen as

> a sacred duty and the source of all human comforts,
> creating wealth and making civilization possible. It
> was a cure for boredom and melancholy, and a remedy
> for vice. It was the only sure route to human happiness,
> bringing health, contentment, and personal fulfilment.
> It structured the day, gave opportunities for sociability
> and companionship, fostered pride in individual cre-
> ativity, and created a sense of personal identity.[8]

There is a rich tradition of theologians and philosophers

who see work in that light – as a character-forming moral duty, a cornerstone of civilisation and a prerequisite for human progress. Idleness, these thinkers believe, is the enemy of the soul. Work staves off sin and vice, keeps us from mischief and from slipping into bad mental states. In short, it is a physical, spiritual and emotional necessity that has wide-ranging social benefits. It is worth adding that, in our increasingly atomised society, our workplaces are often where the majority of our social interaction takes place – it is at work that we can develop companionship and a sense of belonging, encounter gossip and intrigue, and experience human kindness and human drama.

Some see the concentration and perseverance that work requires as an antidote to sorrow. They point to the self-esteem that arises from achievement and the satisfaction we can get from physical exertion. In both ancient and modern thought, not having anything to do is often associated with ennui and melancholia, and a lack of purpose in life. As Thomas emphasises, work can be a distraction, something that 'keeps inner thoughts at bay'.[9] And while this is where we can locate the curative aspect of work, it is also precisely where work's dangers lie. For we can become addicted to work, and ever more of us are. The concept of workaholism was first coined in the 1970s. W. E. Oates describes it as 'the compulsive and uncontrollable need to work incessantly'.[10] At first, a workaholic was defined as someone who spends more than 50 hours a week working, but today the definition includes our general attitude to, and mental preoccupation with, work. It is no exaggeration to say that, as a society, we are obsessed with work, many of us being unable to stop thinking about it or to resist the urge to invest all our time and effort into it. We may prioritise work over other core basic needs, even if that causes serious damage to our relationships, bodies and minds. We may feel anxiety when we aren't working, be fixated on work-related success and live in constant fear of being judged a failure.[11]

What can we do when we fall into this category of 'Sabbathless Satans' who simply cannot stop working? Above all, we must seek to disentangle our sense of self-worth and value from our work. That is much easier said than done, of course, and usually requires therapy or coaching. Once those threads have become intertwined, it is very difficult to pull them apart again. Working all the time is also rooted in a fear of being alone with ourselves and our thoughts and feelings. Many of us find it increasingly hard to *be* rather than to *do*. This is partly because we live in a society that privileges activity, but it also reflects a deeper fear of stillness. What might we discover about ourselves when we stop all our restless doing?

There is a peculiar sadness attached to twenty-first-century work. For work is not just the drug of choice for the workaholic, it is our collective narcotic, a new opiate of the masses. Which brings us to Marx. Marx famously argued that we are alienated from our work for two reasons: first and foremost, because we don't own the means of production, meaning we are often working only to see someone else take the benefit. Secondly, owing to an increasingly complex division of labour, we never get to see the finished product of our efforts anymore.

This last point is perhaps more true than ever in the case of service and information technology work. While technology was supposed to save us from having to perform many tedious jobs and to generate more free time, the opposite has happened. We are working more hours than ever, and many of us perform tasks we believe do not really need to be performed. 'The moral and spiritual damage that comes from this situation is profound', David Graeber writes in *Bullshit Jobs: A Theory* (2018). 'It is a scar across our collective soul.' 'There is something very wrong with what we have made ourselves', he argues. 'We have become a civilization based on work – not even "productive work" but work as an end and meaning in itself. ... It is as if we have collectively acquiesced to our own enslavement.'[12] It is very telling that Marx dreamt of liberation through work in his youth, and liberation from work in his older age. The older Marx was, in that respect at least, clearly the wiser Marx.

X is for Xenia

In the thirteenth century, the Persian Sufi mystic Rumi wrote a poem in which he compares us to a guest house through which numerous visitors pass every day. These visitors are our thoughts and emotions. Some are pleasant, others are not. All are transient, and all must be welcomed when they arrive. Whether we like those visitors or not, we must accept them and practise what the ancient Greeks called 'xenia' – the art of extending hospitality to travellers and strangers. The rules of xenia apply regardless of whether our guests come at a good or a bad moment, are entertaining or a drag, gentle or violent, bear gifts or deplete our resources. Xenia demands that we throw open our doors to strangers, feed, bathe and clothe them, provide them with gifts, let them recover their strength and make sure they get safely to their next destination.

In ancient Greece, xenia was a cherished custom the violation of which constituted a grave moral failing. But hospitality matters in other cultures, too. In many myths and stories from around the world, disguised deities masquerade as strangers in need of shelter to establish their potential host's ethical credentials. The hospitality test allowed the gods to determine the extent of someone's generosity and altruism. Good hosts were rewarded with ample gifts, while bad ones were punished.

Xenia derives from *xenos*, the Greek word for stranger, for above all, the practice was a way of showing love and respect for strangers. Crucially, however, hospitality wasn't a one-sided affair. Hosts had the precious opportunity to learn from their guests. In return for gifts, food and shelter, guests were expected to provide stories, gossip and news from other parts of the world. In that way, they repaid their hosts with insights and wisdom.

Can the notion of xenia help us to view our exhaustion in a different light? Exhaustion will almost certainly feel like an unwanted guest in our house, one that, on the surface, appears only to deplete, drain and diminish us, like the infamous suitors in Homer's *Odyssey*, who literally eat Odysseus out of house and home in his absence, devouring his livestock, guzzling his wine and seeking to woo his wife. It is extremely difficult to see what gifts our exhaustion may have to offer us in return. Our exhaustion may, moreover, be a guest that visits us far too frequently, and at the most inopportune moments. It might even have taken up permanent dominion in our house, like a squatter whom we wish we could evict forever. And yet, we will in all likelihood not only have to learn to live more harmoniously with our unwanted guest, but also learn how to benefit from it. The Buddhist nun Pema Chödron writes: 'Nothing ever goes away until it has taught us what we need to know.'[1] What, then, might our exhaustion have to tell us that would be to our benefit?

Above all, exhaustion is a warning signal from our

overstretched minds and bodies, indicating that we can't keep on doing what we're doing. It tells us that we have reached a limit and that we need to make changes to the way we live. It slows us down when we are going too fast. It also alerts us to our finitude – first and foremost the finitude of our energy, but also the finitude of our lifespan. By reminding us that, as we grow older, our physical and mental strength will diminish, it draws attention to our human frailty, urging us to be more compassionate and gentler with ourselves.

We can also look at our exhaustion as a visitor from the nether regions of our rational mind, the land of irrationality and shadows. It comes bearing news of our inner demons and the battles that are raging between our conflicting desires. The stories it may wish to share with us can be hard to hear, but they are likely to be important, if not potentially curative. Our exhaustion may force us to look again at what is happening in other, less conscious parts of ourselves, and to start to take account of our repressed wishes and deeper patterns.

Our unwanted guest is very likely to continue to visit us, usually when we least want it. As with more troublesome feelings, it is best simply to accept it and to listen to what it may have to tell us. Acceptance and Commitment Therapy (ACT) can help us with this task, for it is based on the three pillars of accepting, observing and letting go. If we want to experience good feelings, such as joy, vitality, connectedness and love, we also have to make room in our lives for less desirable ones, such as sadness, shame and fear. We cannot just cherry-pick good feelings and close the door on those feelings that are more troubling. If we decide to let feelings in, it will have to include all of them, both the positive and the negative. And nor should we seek to fight or repress those troubling feelings when they are already in our house. ACT recommends that we become attentive hosts to all our feelings, cognitions and states of mind – be they good or bad. In that way, we will not waste energy on pointless battles, trying to prevent certain guests from entering, and nor will we shut our doors completely and live a lonely and sterile life.

Our task, then, is to meet our exhaustion at the door with an open mind, inviting it in and listening carefully to what it may have to tell us.

Y is for Yellow

The fifteenth-century Italian humanist Marsilio Ficino (1433–99) associated mental and physical exhaustion with melancholia and the movements of the planets. He was particularly concerned about the gloomy influence of Saturn on those born under its sign. A priest and Neo-Platonist scholar, Ficino had a wide range of interests. They included medicine, music and the occult sciences – in particular, astrology and alchemy. In 1489, he wrote a self-help book for exhausted melancholics called *Three Books on Life*. In this text, Ficino presents many weird and wonderful lists, a wild mixture of alchemical and behavioural cures designed to revitalise sufferers from fatigue, torpor, sluggishness and dullness.

In Ficino's view, melancholic exhaustion was the result of a combination of Saturn's torpid energies and a surplus of black bile. Alongside phlegm, yellow bile and blood, black bile was one of the four essential 'humours' that were thought to make up the human body. Medical wisdom dating back to the ancient world stipulated that the four humours needed to be in perfect balance – otherwise, all kinds of disease and ailments would ensue. Black bile, Ficino writes, 'beclouds the spirit with a mass that is black and dense, terrifies the soul, and dulls the intelligence'. Moreover, it can bring 'sluggishness and torpor by its heavy frigidity'.[1] In that state, we hope for nothing and fear everything.

To counterbalance an excess of black bile, and to temper Saturn's sluggish sway, Ficino compiles long lists of beneficial foods, potions and activities. He praises, for example, the healing powers of sweet lyres and song, and recommends to the exhausted 'the frequent viewing of shining water and of green or red colour, the haunting of gardens and groves and pleasant walks along rivers and through lovely meadows'. Ficino also strongly approves 'of horseback riding, driving, and smooth sailing, but above all, of variety, easy occupations, diversified unburdensome business, and the constant company of agreeable people'.[2]

In addition, he provides numerous alchemical recipes for energising syrups and pills. My favourite is a pill that Ficino calls the 'golden one'. This golden pill is designed to draw out phlegm, blood and black bile, to strengthen the body and to sharpen and illuminate the spirit. The recipe is as follows:

> Take, therefore, twelve grains of gold, especially its leaves if they are pure; one-half dram apiece of frankincense, myrrh, saffron, aloe-wood, cinnamon, citron-peel, Melissa, raw scarlet silk, white ben [campion] and red; one dram apiece of purple roses, of red sandal, or red coral, and of the three sorts of myrobalans (emblic, chebule, and Indic), with an amount of properly washed aloe equal to the weight of all the rest. Make pills with pure wine of the best possible quality.[3]

While Ficino's habit of compiling lengthy lists and recipes may seem amusing to us, his eccentric catalogues had a very serious purpose. A true alchemist at heart, Ficino was always searching for just the right combination of things that may fundamentally transform us – the magic sauce for turning base metal into gold. Finding ways to transform our grey inner lives into brighter, more optimistic states and to rekindle our engagement and energy remains the holy grail of burnout research today. Unfortunately, there are no golden pills we can swallow when we are burnt out. Unlike depression, burnout is not normally treated with psychopharmacological interventions such as Prozac or Xanax. It is not caused by measurable chemical imbalances in our brains, and nor, for that matter, is it caused by a surplus of black bile.

However, regarding the behavioural cures for exhaustion, Ficino's suggestions were spot-on. Because we now know that chronic states of exhaustion have multiple and complex causes, effective modern burnout treatment has to be systemic. Treatments therefore tend to include behavioural and lifestyle interventions that are not far off from those Ficino recommended more than 500 years ago. Nature cures, for example, are high on the list of popular burnout cures – such as walking, forest bathing, freshwater swimming and hiking. No doubt 'smooth sailing' and horseback riding would work, too. It may indeed be wise, then, to try and re-integrate 'the haunting of gardens and groves and pleasant walks along rivers and through lovely meadows' into our lives, where we have the ability and access to do so. Even a short walk around the local park, a trip to feed the ducks or a pause to watch an evening sunset is a start.

Adding variety to our occupations by trying out new things and seeking a more diverse diet of experience is very sensible advice, too. As is Ficino's instruction to seek the company of agreeable people. For many of the stressors in our lives are actually other people – energy vampires who drain and deplete us, people who keep on taking our time and attention and who don't give much back.

Ficino also recommends that we surround ourselves with 'things solar' to replenish our energy. While he means that literally, it is at the same time a beautiful metaphor for all things life-affirming. The solar things, according to Ficino, are 'all those gems and flowers which are called heliotrope because they turn towards the Sun, likewise gold, orpiment and golden colours, chrysolite, carbuncle, myrrh, frankincense, musk, amber, balsam, yellow honey, sweet calamus, saffron, spikenard, cinnamon, aloe-wood and the rest of the spices'. But the solar things also include animals such as the ram, the hawk, the cock, the swan, the lion, the scarab beetle and the crocodile. And, perhaps my absolute favourite, amongst the sunny stuff he also counts 'people who are blond, curly-haired, prone to baldness, and magnanimous'. All these items, Ficino writes, 'can be adapted partly to foods, partly to ointments and fumigations, partly to usages and habits. You should frequently perceive and think about these things and love them above all; you should also get a lot of light.'[4]

Let us compile our own lists of things that delight and restore us, then, and that have the power to transform our dim spirit into something brighter. In cases of severe burnout, it is common not just to assess the stressors in our lives but to do an 'energy audit'. These audits help us to establish what drains our energies and what replenishes them. Our own lists will be completely unique, differing quite dramatically from person to person, also depending on whether we are introverts or extroverts, for example.

Remember the list of favourite things in the famous song from *The Sound of Music* (1965)? It is a beautiful example of a list of energy-restoring 'yellow' things – advocating an alchemical mood-alteration recipe in its own right. While Julie Andrews cherishes roses, kittens, kettles and mittens, we may be equally delighted by the reflection of the moon in the still waters of a black pond, the unexpected sight of a bright, butter-coloured flower, the smell of fresh croissants, and the deep murmuring purr of a happy cat. We may even find beauty in our beasts. For, to paraphrase Andrews, when life stings and we are feeling sad, we can simply remember our favourite yellow things, and we won't feel so bad.

Z is for Zeitgeist

The causes of our exhaustion can be psychological or physical, or both at the same time. The ways in which our minds and bodies interact are highly complex, with our psyche constantly impacting on our biology and vice versa. But our exhaustion is also influenced by wider social and political dynamics. We are, after all, relational beings who are firmly embedded in specific cultural contexts. As such, we are shaped by trends, dominant narratives and the zeitgeist – the prevailing spirit of the times. Whether the culture in which we find ourselves is optimistic or pessimistic about its future, content or anxious about its present, and proud or ashamed about its past affects not only our collective state of mind but also many of the personal decisions that we may make, both small and large.

We may, for example, avoid certain kinds of expenditure when we feel our times are precarious, and cut down on our pleasure-related and social activities. The zeitgeist can colour how we interpret national and international events and how we feel about our future. It can also be visible in more subtle cultural trends. The Nigerian writer Chimamanda Ngozi Adichie observes that cultures that feel their best days are behind them tend to fetishise all that is old: historic and period buildings first and foremost, but also past styles in fashion and furniture, and anything that is retro in spirit. Driven by a nostalgic sense of lost greatness, such cultures tend to fail to grasp the challenges of the present. Cultures that feel their best days are yet to come, by contrast, celebrate that which is new: they may tear down historic buildings without hesitation and replace them with hyper-modern structures that revel in the present and radiate hope for the future.[1]

In the late nineteenth century, exhaustion was specifically understood as a 'disease of civilisation', a cultural malady that impacted directly upon the individual. A sense of cultural dis-ease, it was assumed, manifested in the body and mind of the individual and made them ill. Neurasthenia, which shares many symptoms with modern burnout, was thought to be a by-product of modernity. Acceleration was among the most palpable of modernity's qualities. Many bemoaned the faster pace of life, resulting from advances in transportation and communication technologies such as trains and telegraphy. Others blamed the growing pressures of capitalist competition for their exhaustion, as well as a sense of permanent sensual over-stimulation caused by newspapers, street noise and the general hustle and bustle of city life (see 'U is for Urgency').

The concerns of our nineteenth-century forebears about the impact of new technologies on their physical and mental health may now seem negligible to us. After all, we have had to contend with the very real and wide-ranging social, psychological and behavioural transformations that have been caused by the introduction of email, mobile phones and social media. While our ancestors worried that sitting on fast-moving trains would cause 'railway spine' and put undue pressure on their minds and bodies, we worry about the fact that on public transport everybody's head is permanently bowed, causing 'tech neck', all eyes glued to private screens that present carefully curated materials designed to master our attention. It is as though someone has put a powerful spell on us, convincing us that our devices contain salvation, when in fact all they do is provide endless distraction.

While Americans tended to view industrial progress largely optimistically, many cultural critics in nineteenth-century France and Germany noted a climate of pessimism, ennui and declinism. The French and the Germans feared the negative psychological and social effects not just of new technologies but also of moral and physical 'degeneration' – a kind of reverse evolution resulting in decadence and civilisational decay. Degeneration was thought to be visible in an increase in alcoholism, imbecility and prostitution, as well as in the spread of sexual 'perversions' such as homosexuality. Conservative critics were also concerned about the increasing porousness of traditional class boundaries, and especially about the emancipation of women.[2] In many older medical texts on exhaustion, developments of this kind were named explicitly as key exhaustion generators. For example, the American physician and electrotherapist George M. Beard wrote that nervous exhaustion was caused by various characteristics of the modern age, including 'steam-power, the periodical press, the telegraph, the sciences, and the mental activity of women'.[3] We can see, then, that the literature of exhaustion frequently functions as a vehicle for cultural criticism.

There is never anything arbitrary in our identification of the causes of exhaustion. Often we pin them on social transformations that scare or alarm us.

The impact of wider social and cultural developments on our mental state is hard to measure. And yet few of us would deny being emotionally affected by the general mood of our contemporaries and by news of local, national and world events. The news reminds us of those larger contexts of which we are a part, the fate of others nearby or far away, and matters that concern us as a species, such as the climate emergency. Yet many studies show that consuming news can affect our well-being adversely, especially if we are prone to compulsive headline-checking and doom-scrolling. 'News is to the mind what sugar is to the body', the writer Rolf Dobelli suggests. It is so easy to digest that we can consume it in limitless quantities, and yet it is not only devoid of nourishment but can be toxic.[4]

For the news we are fed is almost unremittingly negative. Studies have shown that it triggers our limbic system and stimulates the release of cortisol, thus deregulating our immune system, inhibiting the release of growth hormones and making us more prone to infections. As well as making us more fearful, aggressive and desensitised to the suffering of others, it can become a source of chronic stress. It can also kill our creativity.[5] In the last couple of years, we have of course been exposed to an endless supply of extremely disturbing news, ranging from Brexit, Trump and the Covid pandemic to the war in Ukraine, as well as the worsening climate emergency. It has become ever more difficult to extract ourselves from the fast-moving cycles of apocalyptic headlines. They have no doubt contributed to our personal sense of exhaustion.

It is fair to say that our concerns about the state of the world have moved from a sense of perceived decline to an awareness of a potentially existential threat to our planetary ecosystem and democratic institutions. Many of our systems seem on the verge of collapse. We live in the age of meta-crisis – a series of interconnected crises that include climate change, a rise in populism in many Western and non-Western democracies, growing social fragmentation and political polarisation, intensifying social inequality and an upsurge in mental health problems. We had only just begun to emerge from a devastating global pandemic when Russia invaded Ukraine – an act of brutal barbarism with as yet unpredictable geopolitical and economic consequences. What we do know is that those consequences are already grave. The war has terminated a decades-long period of peace and stability in Europe, and destroyed hopes for increased international collaboration on the matters that concern us all. It has already resulted in a dramatic increase in the cost of living. Our way of life seems threatened on numerous fronts; everything feels precarious and uncertain. It is hard not to worry about the future, and many of us do so without pause.

The climate crisis is the most pressing of our crises. In its way, it is another tale of exhaustion that is manifest in the depletion of our very own planetary habitat: we are exhausting precious and finite resources in an unsustainable way. It is also visible in a growing fatigue with neo-liberal ideology that puts maximising growth and productivity *über alles* – including our own well-being and that of our vital ecosystems. Even the markets themselves have now declared their loss of faith in this crude creature of the 1980s: in September 2022, Liz Truss's announcement of a radical tax-cutting budget caused dramatic financial turmoil and the crash of the pound in the UK. Highly complex in character, the climate crisis requires coordinated collective action at scale. Scientists have been warning us since the 1970s that we cannot continue to pursue unlimited growth agendas without harming the health of our planet and depleting precious resources.

And yet we have not managed to agree on, let alone make, the necessary behavioural changes to reduce toxic CO_2 and methane emissions in a meaningful way. We know all this and have in fact known it for decades. And yet there remains a gap between insight and action. That gap is, I believe, the primary tragedy of our kind. More often than not, we know exactly what we should do, but find ourselves unable to translate our knowledge into action. This holds true at both the collective and the individual level. We wrestle with what the psychologist Robert Kegan calls our inbuilt 'immunity to change', and are unwilling or unable to let go of our old damaging ways.[6] Often, we feel guilt and shame about our inaction, which further aggravates our state of paralysis. The theologian Saint Augustine had already commented on this paradox in the fourth century CE: 'What is the cause of this monstrous situation?' he wondered. 'The mind commands the body and is instantly obeyed. The mind commands itself and meets resistance.'[7]

We seem to live in an age not only of collective

paralysis, but also of in-betweenness: we know that our current world is coming to an end but are not yet able to see the new one that is emerging. The philosopher Zachary Stein has described our era as a 'time between worlds', a liminal period in which 'one world is ending while another is waiting to be born'.[8] The uncertainty that goes hand in hand with this state of affairs is the cause of much worry. It, too, is a contributing factor to our exhaustion in various ways. In general, human beings like neither change nor uncertainty, for both cost a lot of energy. We are deficient in what the poet John Keats called 'negative capability', the ability to dwell in 'uncertainties, mysteries, doubts, without any irritable reaching after fact and reason'. Not being able to plan and predict our futures, as well as those of our children and grandchildren, is likely to cause us great distress, and is perhaps one of the greatest burdens that many of us have to bear.

To tackle the great challenges of our times, both at a personal and a global level, we have to avoid one pitfall above all: a focus on loss rather than on vision. Loss aversion and lack of a positive alternative vision are the major causes of our immunity to change. It is worth remembering that our unproductive behaviours, large or small, always serve a psychological function. They may distract us from our fear or sadness, and they usually also yield fleeting rewards. If we can see only what we may have to give up rather than what we might gain, we will hold on even more tightly to whatever these secondary gains may be. The same is true if we lack all hope for a better future: in that case, too, it is not at all surprising that we will seek to maximise pleasure in the moment. For what's the point of saving or working towards a better future if we don't believe it will ever manifest? Finally, we may also be fixated on our past – more specifically, on past losses that we somehow wish to fix. This is the core dilemma of the philosopher Walter Benjamin's angel of history:

> This is how one pictures the angel of history. His face is turned toward the past. Where we perceived a chain of events, he sees one single catastrophe which keeps piling wreckage and hurls it in front of his feet. The angel would like to stay, awaken the dead, and make whole what has been smashed. But a storm is blowing from Paradise; it has got caught in his wings with such violence that the angel can no longer close them. This storm irresistibly propels him into the future to which his back is turned, while the pile of debris before him grows skyward. The storm is what we call progress.[9]

How, then, can we turn around, let go of our preoccupation with past wreckage and face our uncertain future more courageously? How can we move from paralysed lamentation to vision, and what could a better future look like in this time between worlds? As the ancient rhetoricians knew well, we are unlikely to change our ways based on cold reasoning and facts alone. Logos (logical reasoning) needs to be complemented with pathos (an appeal to our emotions) and ethos (the credibility and moral competence of the speaker). Lasting behavioural change can only ever be the fruit of a holistic approach that appeals as much to our emotions, imagination and moral sense as it does to our rational faculties. We therefore need new and seductive stories and metaphors, as well as poetry, philosophy, art and song.

What is more, if we want to change the status quo, we need to be able to imagine what could be rather than what is. That entails honing our ability to generate a positive vision of our future selves that differs from our present condition.[10] Psychologists have known for quite some time that only if we have clearly visualised the benefits and rewards of our potential actions will we be able to convince ourselves to embark on difficult and arduous change journeys. Remember the notion of 'dead man's goals' that we saw in 'G is for Ghosts'? We use it in coaching when clients simply wish to give up certain unproductive behaviours, such as overeating, drinking too much alcohol, smoking or spending their lives on Twitter and Instagram. The thing is that pursuing dead man's goals doesn't work. They need to be complemented with a concrete, positive vision – one that is powerful and seductive, and that puts what we have to gain rather than what we are going to lose centre-stage. Recall the sad fate of poor, pallid Bartleby: his core dilemma was that he could not develop such a vision. He was only able to articulate what he didn't want to do anymore. Similarly, when it comes to climate change, the aim of simply preventing our species from going extinct is just not good enough. The question is rather: Why shouldn't we go extinct? What's our vision, and what is our purpose? What exactly might we have to offer, now and in the future, that is worth preserving?

Z is for Zeitgeist

The singer Nick Cave writes that the human condition is above all marked by loss: 'losses of dignity, losses of agency, losses of trust, losses of spirit, losses of direction or faith, and, of course, losses of the ones we love.' Collective grief is our baseline condition. And yet, Cave insists, 'happiness and joy continue to burst through this mutual condition. Life, it seems, is full of an insistent, systemic and irrepressible beauty.' But, Cave writes, 'these moments of happiness are not experienced alone, rather they are almost entirely relational and are dependent on a connection to the Other – be it people, or nature, or art, or God. This is where meaning establishes itself, within the connectedness, nested in our shared suffering.'[11] I can think of no better words with which to end this guide. I hope you will find your connection, and that it will help you to rise again from the ashes of our shared exhaustion, and soar skywards, into the blue.

Notes

Introduction

1. American Psychological Association (APA), 2022 *Trend Report: Stress and Burnout are Everywhere*, 1 January 2022. Online at: www.apa.org/monitor/2022/01/special-burnout-stress.

2. American Psychological Association (APA), *Stress in America: Paying with Our Health*, 4 February 2015. Online at: www.apa.org/news/press/releases/stress/2014/stress-report.pdf.

3. Ben Wigert and Sangeeta Agrawal, 'Employee Burnout, Part 1: The 5 Main Causes', *Gallup Survey*, 12 July 2018. Online at: www.gallup.com/workplace/237059/employee-burnout-part-main-causes.aspx.

4. Christina Maslach, Wilmar Schaufeli, Michael P. Leiter, 'Job Burnout', in S. T. Fiske et al. (eds), *Annual Review of Psychology*, 52 (2001), 397–422.

5. Anna Katharina Schaffner, *Exhaustion: A History* (New York: Columbia University Press, 2016).

6. Anna Katharina Schaffner, *The Art of Self-Improvement: Ten Timeless Truths* (New Haven: Yale University Press, 2021).

7. Josh Cohen, *Not Working: Why We Have to Stop* (London: Granta, 2018), p. 65.

8. Ibid., p. 80.

9. Anne Helen Petersen, 'How Millennials Became the Burnout Generation', BuzzFeed, 5 January 2019. Online at: www.buzzfeednews.com/article/annehelenpetersen/millennials-burnout-generation-debt-work. Petersen later expanded and refined her argument and turned it into a book: Anne Helen

Petersen, *Can't Even: How Millennials Became the Burnout Generation* (London: Chatto & Windus, 2021).

10. Petersen, *Can't Even*, p. 220.

11. Frank Kermode, *The Sense of an Ending: Studies in the Theory of Fiction* (Oxford: Oxford University Press, 1968), pp. 94–5.

12. Jonathan Malesic, *The End of Burnout: Why Work Drains us and How to Build a Better Life* (Oakland, CA: California University Press, 2022), p. 15.

13. Audre Lorde, 'Learning from the 60s' (1982). Online at: www. blackpast.org/african-american-history/1982-audre-lorde-learning-60s/#:~:text=There%20is%20no%20such%20 thing,Martin%20Luther%20King%2C%20Jr.

14. See, for example, Ed Diener, *Culture and Well-Being: The Collected Works of Ed Diener* (New York: Springer, 2009); and Paul Dolan, *Happy Ever After: Escaping the Myth of the Perfect Life* (London: Allen Lane, 2019).

15. Cohen, *Not Working*, p. xxxi.

16. David Foster Wallace, *This is Water: Some Thoughts, Delivered on a Significant Occasion, about Living a Compassionate Life* (New York: Little, Brown & Company, 2009), pp. 3–4.

A is for Acceptance

1. Bayo Akomolafe, 'Listening to the Noise and Leading through Play', *TwentyThirty*, 7 September 2022. Online at: www. twentythirty.com/article/bayo-akomolafe-on-listening-to-the-noise-and-leading-through-play#:~:text=Bayo%20 Akomolafe%3A%20One%20of%20my,repeat%20a%20 cycle%20of%20sameness.

2. Epictetus, *Discourses and Selected Writings*, translated by Robert Dobbin (London: Penguin Classics, 2008), p. 147.

3. Tara Brach, *Radical Acceptance: Awakening the Love that Heals Fear and Shame* (London: Rider, 2003), p. 4.

4. Carl Rogers, *On Becoming a Person: A Therapist's View of Psychotherapy* (New York: Mariner Books, 1995), p. 17.

5. Albert Ellis, *The Myth of Self-Esteem: How Rational Emotive Behavior Therapy Can Change your Life Forever* (London: Prometheus, 2005), p. 160.

6. Albert Ellis, 'How I Learned to Help Clients Feel Better and Get Better', *Psychotherapy: Theory, Research, Practice, Training*, 33 (1996), 149–51; 150.

7. Numerous versions of this popular self-help parable are in circulation on the web. Everyone tells it slightly differently. This version, which I slightly modified, can be found online at: www.thechurning.net/there-are-no-opportunities-or-threats-the-parable-of-the-taoist-farmer/.

B is for Burnout

1. Jonathan Malesic, *The End of Burnout: Why Work Drains us and How to Build a Better Life* (Oakland, CA: California University Press, 2022), p. 3.

2. Quoted from Wilmar Schaufeli, 'Past Performance and Future Perspectives on Burnout Research', *SA Journal of Industrial Psychology*, 29:4 (2003), 1–15; 2.

3. Quoted from Wilmar Schaufeli, Michael P. Leiter, and Christina Maslach, 'Burnout: 35 Years of Research and Practice', *Career Development International*, 14:3 (2009), 204–20; 206.

4. See ibid., p. 214.

5. See, for example, the American Association for Psychology report on stress and burnout from January 2022 by Ashley Abramson. Online at: www.apa.org/monitor/2022/01/special-burnout-stress.

6. Anne Helen Petersen, *Can't Even: How Millennials Became the Burnout Generation* (London: Chatto & Windus, 2021), p. xvi.

7. Ibid., p. 220.

8. See, for example, Christina Maslach, Wilmar B. Schaufeli, and Michael P. Leiter, 'Job Burnout', *Annual Review of Psychology* 52: 1 (2001), 411.

9. Christina Maslach and Michael P. Leiter, *The Truth About Burnout: How Organizations Cause Personal Stress and What to Do About It* (San Francisco: Jossey-Bass, 1997), p. 38.

10. See, for example, Zubin Damania, 'It's Not Burnout, It's Moral Injury', March 2019, YouTube. Online at: www.youtube.com/watch?v=L_1PNZdHq6Q&t=12s.

11. See ICD-11, the WHO's International Classification of Diseases publication, edition 11. Online at: icd.who.int/browse11/l-m/en#/http://id.who.int/icd/entity/129180281.

C is for Capitalism

1. Max Weber, *Die Protestantische Ethik und der Geist des Kapitalismus*, edited and introduced by Dirk Kaesler (Munich: C. H. Beck, 2004). English translation by Talcott Parsons and Anthony Giddens. Online at: www.marxists.org/reference/archive/weber/protestant-ethic/index.htm. Translations slightly modified.

2. Ibid., pp. 190–91.

3. Ibid., pp. 183–4.

D is for Dante

1. Dante Alighieri, 'Hell', Canto III, *The Divine Comedy: The Vision of Hell, Purgatory, and Paradise*. Translated by H. F. Cary. Available online at: https://www.gutenberg.org/cache/epub/8800/pg8800-images.html#cantoI.3. All quotations in this chapter are from this edition.

2. Ibid., 'Hell', Canto I.

3. Ibid. 'Hell', Canto I.

4. Ibid., 'Hell', Canto VII.

5. Ibid., 'Hell', Canto XXIV.

6. Ibid., 'Purgatory', Canto XII.

Notes

E is for Energy

1. Anonymous, *The Yellow Emperor's Classic of Medicine*, translated by Maoshing Ni (Boston and London: Shambhala, 1995), p. 7.

F is for Failure

1. Samuel Beckett, *Company / Ill Seen Ill Said / Worstward Ho / Stirrings Still*, edited by Dirk van Hulle (London: Faber & Faber, 2009), p. 81.
2. Maya Angelou interviewed by Marianne Schell, *Psychology Today*, 17 February 2009. Online at: www.psychologytoday. com/gb/blog/the-guest-room/200902/interview-maya-angelou.
3. Matthew Syed, *Black Box Thinking: Marginal Gains and the Secrets of High Performance* (London: John Murray, 2015), p. 10; p. 11.
4. Antonio Machado, 'Last Night as I was Sleeping', in *Times Alone: Selected Poems by Antonio Machado*. Translated by Robert Bly (Middletown, CT: Wesleyan University Press, 1983), p. 43.

G is for Ghosts

1. Herman Melville, 'Bartleby, the Scrivener', in *Billy Budd, Sailor, and Selected Tales*, edited by Robert Milder (Oxford: Oxford University, 1998), pp. 1–41; p. 4 and p. 6.
2. Ibid., p. 4.
3. Ibid., p. 10.
4. Ibid., p. 21.
5. Ibid., p. 40.
6. Ibid., p. 10; p. 11; p. 19.
7. John C. Parkin, *F**K It: The Ultimate Spiritual Way* (New York: Hay House, 2014), p. 1. Other books of that kind include Sarah Knight's *The Life-Changing Magic of Not Giving a F**k* (2015) and Mark Manson's *The Subtle Art of Not Giving a F*ck* (2016).

8. Parkin, *F**K It: The Ultimate Spiritual Way*, p. 18.

H is for Heaviness

1. Dante Alighieri, 'Purgatory', Canto IV, *The Divine Comedy: The Vision of Hell, Purgatory, and Paradise*. Translated by H. F. Cary. Available online at: https://www.gutenberg.org/cache/epub/8800/pg8800-images.html#cantoI.3.

I is for Inner Critic

1. Tara Brach, *Radical Acceptance: Awakening the Love that Heals Fear and Shame* (London: Rider, 2003), p. 4.
2. Sigmund Freud, 'Mourning and Melancholia', in *The Standard Edition of the Complete Psychological Works of Sigmund Freud*, edited and translated by J. Strachey, vol. XIV (London: Vintage, 2001), pp. 237–60.
3. See Shirzad Chamine, *Positive Intelligence: Why only 20% of Teams and Individuals Achieve their True Potential and How you can Achieve Yours* (Austin, TX: Greenleaf, 2012), p. 212, and Steve Peters, *The Chimp Paradox: The Mind Management Programme for Confidence, Success and Happiness* (London: Vermilion, 2012).
4. A. T. Beck, A. Freeman & D. Davis, *Cognitive Therapy of Personality Disorders* (3rd edn) (New York: Guilford, 2015).
5. David Burns, *Feeling Good: The New Mood Therapy* (New York: New American Library, 1980).
6. S. C. Hayes, K. Strosahl & K. G. Wilson, *Acceptance and Commitment Therapy: An Experiential Approach to Behavior Change* (New York: Guilford, 1999).
7. Russ Harris, *The Happiness Trap. Based on ACT: A Revolutionary Mindfulness-Based Programme for Overcoming Stress, Anxiety and Depression* (London: Robinson, 2008).

J is for Joy

1. See, for example, Ciara McCabe, 'The Science Behind Why Hobbies Can Improve Our Mental Health', The Conversation,

11 February 2021. Online at: theconversation.com/the-science-behind-why-hobbies-can-improve-our-mental-health-153828.

2. Anne Helen Petersen, *Can't Even: How Millennials Became the Burnout Generation* (London: Chatto & Windus, 2021), p. 198.

3. Oliver Burkeman, *Four Thousand Weeks: Time Management for Mortals* (London: Vintage, 2021), p. 158.

4. Quoted from Keith Thomas (ed.), *The Oxford Book of Work* (Oxford: Oxford University Press, 1999), p. 260.

K is for Kaizen

1. Sarah Harvey, *Kaizen: The Japanese Method for Transforming Habits One Small Step at a Time* (London: Bluebird, 2019).

2. See ibid., pp. 14–16.

3. See Angela Duckworth, *Grit: Why Passion and Resilience are the Secrets to Success* (London: Vermilion, 2017).

4. Carol S. Dweck, *Mindset: Changing the Way You Think to Fulfil Your Potential* (London: Robinson, 2017).

5. Ibid., p. 7.

6. Jonathan Rowson, *The Moves that Matter: A Chess Grandmaster on the Game of Life* (London: Bloomsbury, 2019), p. xx.

L is for Life-Cost

1. Henri David Thoreau, *Walden* (London: Penguin, 2016), p. 11.

2. Ibid., p. 13.

3. Ibid., p. 7.

4. Ibid., p. 86.

5. Ibid., p. 85.

6. Quoted in Cal Newport, *Digital Minimalism: On Living Better with Less Technology* (London: Penguin Business, 2019), p. 39.

7. 'What is Voluntary Simplicity?' by The Simplicity

Collective. Online at: simplicitycollective.com/start-here/
what-is-voluntary-simplicity-2.

8. Duane Elgin, *Voluntary Simplicity: Toward a Way of Life
that is Outwardly Simple, Inwardly Rich* (New York: William
Morrow, 1983), pp. 33–4.

9. 'What is Voluntary Simplicity?' by The Simplicity
Collective. Online at: simplicitycollective.com/start-here/
what-is-voluntary-simplicity-2.

10. Tim Kasser, *The High Price of Materialism* (Cambridge,
Massachusetts: The MIT Press, 2002).

M is for Memento Mori

1. Marcus Aurelius, *Meditations*, translated by Martin
Hammond (London: Penguin, 2006), pp. 17, 32.

2. Psalms 90:12.

3. Eckhart Tolle, *The Power of Now: A Guide to Spiritual
Enlightenment* (London: Hodder & Stoughton, 1999), p. 40.

N is for Narratives

1. See Anna Katharina Schaffner, *Exhaustion: A History* (New
York: Columbia University Press, 2016).

2. Aristotle, *Problems*, translated by W. S. Hett, 2 vols
(Cambridge, MA: Harvard University Press, 1957), vol. II,
p. 155.

3. See John Cassian, *The Monastic Institutes,* translated by Edgar
C. S. Gibson, in *A Select Library of Nicene and Post-Nicene
Fathers of the Christian Church*, edited by Henry Wace and
Philip Schaff, 14 vols (Oxford: James Parker and Company;
New York: The Christian Literature Company, 1894), vol. XI,
second series, pp. 183–641; Siegfried Wenzel, *The Sin of Sloth:
Acedia in Medieval Thought and Literature* (Chapel Hill:
University of North Carolina Press, 1967); and Werner Post,
*Acedia – Das Laster der Trägheit. Zur Geschichte der siebten
Todsünde* (Freiburg and Vienna: Herder, 2011).

4. Quoted in Wenzel, *The Sin of Sloth*, p. 5.
5. See ibid., p. 32.
6. Cassian, *The Monastic Institutes*, vol. XI, second series, pp. 183–641; p. 266.
7. Ibid., p. 267.
8. Ibid.
9. Ibid.
10. Geoffrey Chaucer, 'The Parson's Tale', in *The Canterbury Tales*, translated into Modern English by Eugene J. Crook (1993). Online at: https://english3.fsu.edu/canterbury/parson. html. Translation slightly revised.
11. See Wenzel, *The Sin of Sloth*, p. 22.
12. See George M. Beard, *A Practical Treatise on Nervous Exhaustion (Neurasthenia): Its Symptoms, Nature, Sequences, Treatment* (New York: W. Wood, 1880); and *American Nervousness: Its Causes and Consequences. A Supplement to Nervous Exhaustion (Neurasthenia)* (New York: G. P. Putnam's Sons, 1881).
13. Beard, *American Nervousness*, p. vi.
14. See Janet Oppenheim, *'Shattered Nerves': Doctors, Patients, and Depression in Victorian England* (New York and Oxford: Oxford University Press, 1991), p. 81.
15. Beard, *American Nervousness*, p. 26.

O is for Oblomov

1. Ivan Goncharov, *Oblomov*, translated by Natalie Duddington (New York: Alfred A. Knopf, 1992).
2. Ibid., p. 196.
3. Ibid., p. 205.
4. Josh Cohen, *Not Working: Why We Have to Stop* (London: Granta, 2018), p. xviii.
5. Ibid., p. 76.
6. Oliver Burkeman, *Four Thousand Weeks: Time Management for Mortals* (London: Vintage, 2021), p. 30.

P is for Perfectionism

1. J. Stoeber & L. E. Damian, 'Perfectionism in Employees: Work Engagement, Workaholism, and Burnout', in F. M. Sirois & D. S. Molnar (eds), *Perfectionism, Health, and Well-Being.* (New York: Springer, 2016), pp. 265–83.

2. Ibid.

3. See J. Stoeber & K. Otto, 'Positive Conceptions of Perfectionism: Approaches, Evidence, Challenges', *Personality and Social Psychology Review*, 10 (2006), 295–319.

4. See, for example, S. B. Sherry et al., 'Perfectionism Dimensions and Research Productivity in Psychology Professors: Implications for Understanding the (Mal)Adaptiveness of Perfectionism', *Canadian Journal of Behavioural Science*, 42 (2010), 273–83.

5. The School of Life, *On Self-Hatred: Learning to Like Oneself* (London: The School of Life, 2022), p. 47.

6. See J. Stoeber & K. Otto, 'Positive Conceptions of Perfectionism: Approaches, Evidence, Challenges'.

7. The School of Life, *On Self-Hatred*, p. 48.

8. See, for example, P. E. Flaxman, J. Ménard, F. W. Bond & G. Kinman, 'Academics' Experiences of a Respite from Work: Effects of Self-Critical Perfectionism and Perseverative Cognition on Postrespite Well-Being', *Journal of Applied Psychology*, 97 (2012), 854–65; and J. K. Mitchelson, 'Seeking the Perfect Balance: Perfectionism and Work-Family Conflict', *Journal of Occupational and Organizational Psychology*, 82 (2009), 349–67.

9. See, for example, R. J. Burke, 'Workaholism in Organizations: Psychological and Physical Well-Being Consequences', *Stress Medicine*, 16 (2000), 11–16; R. Snir & I. Harpaz, 'The Workaholism Phenomenon: A Cross-National Perspective', *Career Development International*, 11 (2006), 374–93; and T. W. H. Ng, K. L. Sorensen & D. C. Feldman, 'Dimensions, Antecedents, and Consequences of Workaholism: A

Notes

Conceptual Integration and Extension', *Journal of Organizational Behavior*, 28 (2007), 111–36.

10. K. M. Matuska, 'Workaholism, Life Balance, and Well-Being: A Comparative Analysis', *Journal of Occupational Science*, 17 (2010), 104–11.

11. See J. Stoeber & L. E. Damian, 'Perfectionism in Employees: Work Engagement, Workaholism, and Burnout'.

12. Tara Brach, *Radical Acceptance: Awakening the Love that Heals Fear and Shame* (London: Rider, 2003), p. 21.

Q is for Qi

1. Nancy N. Chen, '*Qi* in Asian Medicine', in *Energy Medicine East and West: A Natural History of Qi*, edited by David Mayor and Marc S. Micozzi (New York: Churchill Livingstone Elsevier, 2011), pp. 3–10; p. 3.

2. David Mayor, 'Elemental Souls and Vernacular *Qi*: Some Attributes of What Moves Us', in *Energy Medicine East and West*, pp. 23–47; p. 24; Chen, '*Qi* in Asian Medicine', p. 3.

3. Ted J. Kaptchuk, *Chinese Medicine: The Web that Has No Weaver*, revised and expanded edition (London: Rider, 2000), p. 47.

4. Ibid., pp. 240–41.

5. Anon., *The Yellow Emperor's Classic of Medicine*, translated by Maoshing Ni (Boston and London: Shambhala, 1995), p. 149.

6. Ibid., p. 150.

7. Ibid., p. xiii.

8. Ibid., p. 59.

9. Ibid., p. 258.

10. See Richard E. Nisbett, *The Geography of Thought: How Asians and Westerners Think Differently – And Why* (New York: The Free Press, 2003), pp. 31–34.

11. See Paul U. Unschuld, *Traditionelle Chinesische Medizin* (Munich: C. H. Beck, 2013), p. 28; p. 49.

12. See Will Storr, *Selfie: How We Became So Self-Obsessed and What It's Doing to Us* (London: Picador, 2017), pp. 66–7.

R is for Rest

1. Exodus 20:8–11.
2. For more on the topic of rest, see Anna Katharina Schaffner, *Exhaustion: A History* (New York: Columbia University Press, 2016), pp. 132–49.
3. Matthew Walker, *Why We Sleep: The New Science of Sleep and Dreams* (London: Allen Lane, 2017).
4. See, for example, L. Stojanovich & D. Marisavljevich, 'Stress as a Trigger of Autoimmune Disease', *Autoimmunity Reviews*, 7 (2008), 209–13, and P. H. Wirtz & R. von Känel, 'Psychological Stress, Inflammation, and Coronary Heart Disease', *Current Cardiology Reports*, 19 (2017), 1–10.
5. Robert Poynton, *Do Pause: You are not a To Do list* (Cardigan: The Do Book Co., 2019).
6. Silas Weir Mitchell, *Fat and Blood and How to Make Them*, edited and introduced by Michael S. Kimmel (New York and Oxford, Altamira Press, 2004), p. 9.
7. Ibid., pp. 18–19.
8. See Claudia Hammond, *The Art of Rest: How to Find Respite in the Modern Age* (London: Canongate, 2019).
9. See Anna Katharina Schaffner, *The Art of Self-Improvement: Ten Timeless Truths* (New Haven: Yale University Press, 2021), pp. 127–30.
10. Ibid., p. 103.
11. See, for example, Richard Mabey, *Nature Cure* (London: Chatto & Windus, 2005); Isabel Hardman, *The Natural Health Service: What the Great Outdoors can do for Your Mind* (London: Atlantic Books, 2020); Dr Quing Li, *Shinrin-Yoku: The Art and Science of Forest Bathing* (London: Penguin Life, 2018); Professor Yoshifumi Miyazaki, *Shinrin-yoku: The Japanese Way of Forest Bathing for Health and*

Relaxation (London: Aster, 2018); Nick Barker, *ReWild: The Art of Returning to Nature* (London: Aurum Press, 2017); and Simon Barnes, *Rewild Yourself: 23 Spellbinding Ways to Make Nature More Visible* (London: Simon & Schuster, 2018).

12. Examples include Anthony Storr's *Solitude* (London: HarperCollins, 1997); Anneli Rufus's *Party of One: The Loners' Manifesto* (New York: Marlowe & Company, 2003); Sara Maitland's *How To Be Alone* (London: Macmillan, 2014); Michael Harris's *Solitude: In Pursuit of a Singular Life in a Crowded World* (New York: Random House, 2018) and Erling Kagge's *Silence: In the Age of Noise* (London: Penguin, 2018).

S is for Stoicism

1. See, for example, Ryan Holiday, *The Obstacle is the Way: The Ancient Art of Turning Adversity to Advantage* (London: Profile, 2014) and Massimo Pigliucci, *How to be a Stoic: Ancient Wisdom for Modern Living* (London: Rider, 2017).

2. For more on Stoicism, see Anna Katharina Schaffner, *The Art of Self-Improvement: Ten Timeless Truths* (New Haven: Yale University Press, 2021), pp. 37–48.

3. Seneca, *Letters from a Stoic: Epistulae Morales ad Lucilium*, translated by Robin Campbell (London: Penguin, 2004), p. 15.

4. Ibid., p. 230.

5. See Russ Harris, *The Happiness Trap: Stop Struggling, Start Living*, revised and updated edition (London: Robinson, 2022).

6. See Martin Seligman, *Learned Optimism: How to Change Your Mind and Your Life* (London, Boston: Nicholas Brealey Publishing, 2006).

7. See Richard E. Nisbett, *The Geography of Thought: How Asians and Westerners Think Differently – and Why* (London: Nicholas Brealey, 2003).

8. Seneca, *Letters*, p. 69.

9. Epictetus, *Of Human Freedom*, translated by Robert Dobbin (London: Penguin, 2010), p. 14.
10. Ibid., p. 52.
11. Marcus Aurelius, *Meditations*, translated by Martin Hammond (London: Penguin, 2006), pp. 48.
12. Ibid., p. 113.
13. Ibid., p. 31.
14. See Norman Doidge, *The Brain That Changes Itself: Stories of Personal Triumph from the Frontiers of Brain Science* (London: Penguin, 2008).
15. John Sharp, *The Insight Cure: Change your Story, Transform your Life* (London: Hay House, 2018), p. xxi.

T is for Time
1. E. P. Thompson, 'Time, Work-Discipline, and Industrial Capitalism', *Past & Present*, 38, 1967, 56–97.
2. David Graeber, *Bullshit Jobs: A Theory* (London: Allen Lane, 2018), p. 92.
3. Thompson, 'Time, Work-Discipline, and Industrial Capitalism', p. 56.
4. Ibid., p. 91.
5. Ibid., p. 93.
6. John O'Donohue, 'For One Who Is Exhausted', in *Benedictus* (London: Bantam Press, 2007), pp. 140–41. Reprinted with permission from Penguin Random House.

U is for Urgency
1. Hartmut Rosa, *Social Acceleration: A New Theory of Modernity*, translated by Jonathan Trejo-Mathys (New York: Columbia University Press, 2015).
2. Karl Marx and Friedrich Engels, *The Communist Manifesto* (1848). Online at: www.marxists.org/archive/marx/works/1848/communist-manifesto/cho1.htm.
3. Friedrich Nietzsche, *The Gay Science*, 1882, rev. 1887,

translated by Walter Kaufmann (London: Random House, 1974), p. 259.

4. See Anna Katharina Schaffner, *Exhaustion: A History* (New York: Columbia University Press, 2016), pp. 85–110.

5. Heinrich Mann, 'Doktor Biebers Versuchung', in *Haltlos: Sämtliche Erzählungen I* (Frankfurt am Main: S. Fischer, 1995), pp. 494–550; p. 522. My translation.

6. Wilhelm Erb, *Über die wachsende Nervosität unserer Zeit* (Heidelberg: J. Hörning, 1884), p. 20. My translation.

7. Anonymous, *The Yellow Emperor's Classic of Medicine*, translated by Maoshing Ni (Boston and London: Shambhala, 1995), p. 1.

8. Quoted in Oliver Burkeman, *Four Thousand Weeks: Time Management for Mortals* (London: Vintage, 2021), pp. 166–9.

9. Franz Kafka, 'Reflections on Sin, Pain, Hope and the True Way', in *The Great Wall of China: Stories and Reflections* (New York: Schocken Books, 1970), p. 87.

10. See Burkeman, who makes a similar argument in *Four Thousand Weeks*.

V is for Vampires

1. Arlie Russell Hochschild with Anne Machung, *The Second Shift: Working Families and the Revolution at Home*, revised edition (New York: Penguin, 2012).

2. See, for example, Peg Streep, *Daughter Detox: Recovering from an Unloving Mother and Reclaiming your Life* (New York: Ile D'Espoir Press, 2017).

3. Quoted in anonymous, 'Grey Rocking: How to Bore a Toxic Narcissist out of Your Life', *The Guardian*, 31 August 2022. Online at: www.theguardian.com/science/2022/aug/31/grey-rocking-how-to-bore-a-toxic-narcissist-out-of-your-life.

4. See Jean M. Twenge and W. Keith Campbell, *The Narcissism Epidemic: Living in the Age of Entitlement* (New York: Atria, 2013).

5. Quoted from Matthieu Ricard, *Altruism: The Science and Psychology of Kindness*, translation anonymous (London: Atlantic, 2015), pp. 293–4.

W is for Work
1. Jonathan Malesic, *The End of Burnout: Why Work Drains us and How to Build a Better Life* (Oakland, CA: California University Press, 2022), p. 3.
2. Robin I. M. Dunbar, 'The Social Brain Hypothesis', *Evolutionary Anthropology*, vol. 6, 1998, 178–90.
3. See, for example, blog.moderngov.com/2019/02/how-much-time-do-we-spend-at-work.
4. Keith Thomas, 'Preface', in *The Oxford Book of Work*, edited by Keith Thomas (Oxford: Oxford University Press, 1999), pp. v–vii.
5. See ibid.
6. Genesis 3:17–19.
7. See Thomas, 'Preface', *The Oxford Book of Work*, p. xviii.
8. Ibid., p. xvii.
9. Ibid., p. xxii.
10. W. E. Oates, *Confessions of a Workaholic: The Facts about Work Addiction* (New York: World, 1971).
11. C. Balducci, P. Spagnoli & M. Clark, 'Advancing Workaholism Research', *International Journal of Environmental Research and Public Health*, vol. 17, 2020, 9435.
12. David Graeber, *Bullshit Jobs: A Theory* (London: Allen Lane, 2018), p. xxiv.

X is for Xenia
1. Pema Chödron, *When Things Fall Apart: Heart Advice in Difficult Times* (London: HarperNonFiction, 2005), p. 88.

Y is for Yellow
1. Marsilio Ficino, *Three Books on Life: A Critical Edition and Translation with Introduction and Notes*, edited by Carol V.

Notes

Kaske and John R. Clark, Medieval & Renaissance Texts & Studies, vol. 57 (Tempe, Arizona: Medieval & Renaissance Texts & Studies, 1989), p. 117–18.

2. Ibid., pp. 135–7.
3. Ibid., p. 149.
4. Ibid., p. 249.

Z is for Zeitgeist

1. Chimamanda Ngozi Adichie, *Americanah* (London: Fourth Estate, 2014).
2. See Anna Katharina Schaffner, *Modernism and Perversion: Sexual Deviance in Sexology and Literature, 1850–1930* (Basingstoke: Palgrave Macmillan, 2012).
3. George M. Beard, *American Nervousness: Its Causes and Consequences* (New York: G. P. Putnam's Sons, 1881), p. vi.
4. Rolf Dobelli, 'News is bad for you – and giving up reading it will make you happier', *The Guardian*, 12 April 2013. Online at: www.theguardian.com/media/2013/apr/12/news-is-bad-rolf-dobelli.
5. See ibid.
6. Robert Kegan and Lisa Laskow Lahey, *Immunity to Change: How to Overcome it and Unlock the Potential in Yourself and Your Organization* (Boston: Harvard Business Press, 2009).
7. Saint Augustine, *Confessions,* translated by Henry Chadwick (Oxford: Oxford University Press, 2008), p. 147.
8. Zachary Stein, 'Education Must Make History Again', in *Perspectiva*, 27 January 2022. Online at: systems-souls-society.com/education-must-make-history-again/.
9. Walter Benjamin, 'Theses on the Philosophy of History', in *Illuminations*, translated by Harry Zohn (New York: Schocken Books, 1969), p. 249.
10. See, for example, Rob Hopkins, *From What Is to What If: Unleashing the Power of Imagination to Create the Future We Want* (Hartford, VT: Chelsea Green Publishing, 2019).

11. Nick Cave, 'What is the Point in Life?', *The Red Hand Files*, September 2022. Online at: www.theredhandfiles.com/ what-is-the-point-in-life/.